Connections for Comprehension

C

CURRICULUM ASSOCIATES®, Inc.

To the Student

When you read, you think about *what* you read. But does the meaning go beyond the page? Does what you read have real meaning for you? *Connections for Comprehension* will help you see how reading is connected to you and to the world around you.

Connections for Comprehension Book C has 6 fiction stories and 6 nonfiction selections that will capture your interest. You will read and then you will answer questions that will help you understand and enjoy what you have read. And you will make some very interesting connections.

So start making connections now!

Acknowledgments

Product Development

Program Developer and Editor: Dale Lyle
Writer: Jeanine Jenks Farley
Reviewer: Mary McNary

Design and Production

Designer and Illustrator: Susan Hawk
Typesetter: Yvonne Cronin

Photo Credits

Page 43: National Archives and Records Administration
Page 44: Library of Congress, Prints and Photographs Division, LC-USZ6-1248
Page 45: National Archives and Records Administration
Page 102: Library of Congress, Prints and Photographs Division, LC-USZ62-78374

Illustration Credits

Pages 7–9, 12–14, 25–27, 30–32, 48–50, 79–81, 97: Susan Hawk
Pages 98–99: Pat Lucas

Table of **Contents**

UNIT 1   FICTION ⟷ FICTION

Preview Unit 1

The two selections in Unit 1 are fiction.

In Lesson 1, you will read a PLAY, *The Fox and the Goat*.

In Lesson 2, you will read a REALISTIC FICTION story, "Alex's Soggy Day."

The two selections in Unit 1 share the theme of *looking before you leap*.

In Lesson 3, you will make connections:

text to self

text to text

text to world

Fiction comes from a writer's imagination. The stories are made up. The purpose of fiction stories is to entertain. Most fiction stories have the following elements and form:

- **Setting:** The setting is when and where a story happens.

- **Characters:** The characters are the people or animals in the story.

- **Problem:** The problem is something that the characters must face and solve.

- **Plot Events:** The events are what the characters do to solve the problem. The events are the action.

- **Resolution:** The resolution is the "end," when the characters have solved the problem.

As you read the stories in Unit 1, pay special attention to these elements: **Characters** and **Problem**.

- **Characters:** Characters are the people or animals in a story. An author may show what a character is like through what the character looks like or through the character's actions, thoughts, or goals. What the character says and what the character thinks of other characters also tells what the character is like.

- **Problem:** All fiction stories have a setting, characters, a problem, plot events, and a resolution. The problem is something that the main character faces and solves by the end of the story. Other characters take part in solving the problem, too.

Fiction stories can have certain features. As you read the selections in Unit 1, pay special attention to these features: **Dialogue** and **Stage Directions**.

- **Dialogue:** Fiction stories and plays may contain dialogue. Dialogue is the words that the characters say to each other. In most fiction stories, the actual words that a character says are in quotation marks. In a play, the words that a character says follow the character's name in the script, which tells the story.

- **Stage Directions:** In a play, these are the words in parentheses and in italic, or slanted type (*like this*) in the script. These words tell what the actors do on stage. They also tell the actors how to say a line of dialogue. In a story, this kind of information is part of the story itself.

LESSON 1: Play
The Fox and the Goat

Get Ready to Read

Learn About Plays

The Fox and the Goat is a play.

> Plays are like fiction. They are stories that are acted out on stage. Like other stories, plays have characters, a setting, a problem, a plot, and a resolution. The characters in a play talk to each other through dialogue. They follow the words in a script. Stage directions tell how the stage should look. They also tell how the actors should speak, move, or act on stage.

Think About Vocabulary

When you read this play, you may come across some new words. You may also find words used in unusual ways. Here are two words for you to know before you read.

well: a deep hole that is dug into the ground until water is reached
ledge: a ridge that forms a shelf on a cliff or rock wall

As you read the play, circle at least three more words. Write the words and what they mean in the play. Use a dictionary to check each meaning.

Show What You Know

This play is about a fox and a goat. What do you know about foxes? What do you know about goats? Complete the diagram. In the left part, tell one way that foxes are different from goats. In the right part, tell one way that goats are different from foxes. The middle tells how foxes and goats are alike.

You can add to the diagram after you read the play.

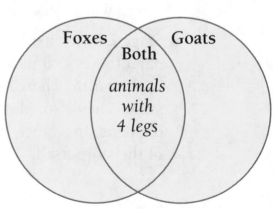

Foxes · Goats · **Both** · *animals with 4 legs*

Read *The Fox and the Goat*

Read this version of a **play** from long ago. Think about the details that make it a play. Pay attention to the stage directions. They tell about what the actors do on stage and how they say some lines. Also think about the characters, the problem they face, and the dialogue they use.

The Fox and the Goat

Characters
A fox with a bushy red tail
A goat with very long horns and a beard

(A fox walks along a forest path.)

Fox: What a lovely day! Oooooops! What's happening! Oh!

*(The fox falls into an old **well** and lands in a deep pool of water.)*

Fox: *(coughing and sputtering)* Oh my! I seem to have fallen down a well. I was too busy looking at the sky to see where I was stepping. Oh! Oh! This water is cold.

(The fox paddles around helplessly in the water for a few minutes.)

Fox: It's dark down here, but I think I see a **ledge** on the side of the well. Maybe I can swim over to it.

(The fox struggles in the water.)

Fox: If foxes were meant to swim, we would have flippers. Oh! Oh! Good! I have made it to the ledge.

(The fox puts his front paws on the ledge.)

Fox: That's it. Almost out. There! I did it. Now I'll just sit here and dry off for a spell.

(After a while the fox looks up.)

Fox: The sides of this well certainly are steep. How can I get out?

(The fox tries to climb up the side of the well but falls down.)

Fox: How will I ever get out of here? I'm wet. I'm cold. I'm hungry. I need a plan.

(Just then a very thirsty goat walks along the forest path near the well.)

Fox: Who is up there?

Goat: *(looking into the well)* Is the water good down there?

Fox: *(lavishly praising the water)* Haven't you heard? This is the best water in the land. Why don't you come down and taste it for yourself?

(Without thinking, the goat jumps into the well and lands in the water.)

Goat: Help! Help! I can't swim.

Fox: Grab my bushy tail. I will pull you out of the water.

(The goat grabs the fox's tail.)

Goat: Pull! Pull!

Fox: I'm pulling as hard as I can. You're almost out. There!

(The goat climbs onto the ledge.)

Goat: I don't know what I would have done without you.

Fox: I'm glad I could help a fellow forest creature.

Goat: I was thirsty when I jumped down, but now I think I've swallowed half an ocean. How do we get out?

Fox: That, my friend, is the problem. There is no way out. The walls are too steep to climb.

Goat: There must be something we can do.

Fox: Let me think.

(The fox pretends to be deep in thought.)

Fox: Aha! I know. If you put your front feet on the side of wall, I will run up your back and onto your horns. From the top of your horns I might be able to jump out of the well. When I get out of the well, I will give you my tail to grab. Then I will pull you out of the well, too.

Goat: What a splendid idea!

FICTION & FICTION

(The goat puts his front paws on the wall of the well. The fox climbs onto the goat's back and stands on his horns. The fox jumps out of the well and runs off.)

Goat: Wait! Wait! You promised to help me get out.

Fox: You foolish fellow! My tail is not nearly long enough to reach you way down there at the bottom of the well. If you had any sense, you would never have jumped down in the first place. Couldn't you see that there was no way out?

Moral: Look before you leap.

Tell It in Your Words

Briefly retell the play *The Fox and the Goat* in your own words. Tell who the characters are. Tell what happens in the story. Tell how the story ends.

_____

_____

_____

_____

_____

_____

_____

_____

Check Your Understanding

Answer these questions to see how well you understood the play
The Fox and the Goat. Circle the answers.

1. What is this play mostly about?
   A a steep well and a careless fox
   B a fox and a goat who are trapped
      in a well
   C a thirsty goat who walks along
      a forest path
   D a fox that is thirsty

2. Reread page 8 where the fox tells
   the goat about the water.
   What does *lavishly* mean?
   A grumpily   C sadly
   B greatly   D angrily

3. Which of the following *best* completes
   the character web of the fox?

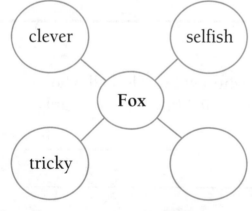

   A silly   C dishonest
   B honest   D jolly

4. How do you know that this is a play
   and not another kind of story?
   A It has a problem.
   B It has characters.
   C It has a setting.
   D It has stage directions.

5. What could be another good title
   for this play?
   A *The Fox, the Goat, and the Well*
   B *The Fox and the Forest*
   C *The Thirsty Goat*
   D *The Bushy-Tailed Fox*

6. Why do you think the fox told the
   goat that the water was the best
   in the land?
   A The fox wanted his friend to drink
      the best-tasting water in the area.
   B The fox wanted the goat to drink
      the well dry.
   C The fox wanted the goat to come
      down so the fox could climb up
      the goat's back.
   D The fox wanted the goat to throw
      him a rope.

7. In the play, how are the fox and the
   goat different?
   A The goat is smart. The fox is not.
   B The fox is clever. The goat is not.
   C The fox is trapped. The goat
      is not.
   D The goat gets wet. The fox
      does not.

8. What is the fox's problem in this play?
   A He can't share the water with
      the goat.
   B He is trapped in a well and wants
      to get out.
   C He doesn't like the goat.
   D He doesn't like water.

LESSON 2: Realistic Fiction "Alex's Soggy Day"

Get Ready to Read

Learn About Realistic Fiction

"Alex's Soggy Day" is a realistic fiction story.

> Realistic fiction stories are about people, places, and things that could be real. The stories are made up, but they sound like they could have happened in real life. Every part of the story could happen to real people. The characters are ordinary people who solve a believable problem.

Think About Vocabulary

When you read this story, you may come across some new words. You may also see words used in unusual ways. Here are three words for you to know before you read.

impulsive: acting quickly without thinking about what might happen
hasty: acting too quickly
bedraggled: wet and muddy

As you read the story, circle at least three more words. Write the words and what they mean in the story. Use a dictionary to check each meaning.

Show What You Know

The boys in this story are good friends. What do you know about friendship? List your ideas. Put the most important ideas first. Put the least important ideas last.

1. _____   3. _____
2. _____   4. _____

You can add to your list after you read the story.

Read "Alex's Soggy Day"

This story is about two friends, Desi and Alex. One of the two learns a lesson. Read the story to find out what lesson he learns.

As you read the story, think about the details that make it a **realistic fiction** story. Also think about the characters, the problem they face, and the dialogue they use.

Alex's Soggy Day

Desi and Alex were the best of friends. Desi was careful and thoughtful, while Alex was **impulsive** and **hasty**. Although the two boys were very different, they enjoyed each other's company immensely.

One day the two were walking through a neighborhood park after a sudden rain shower. They explored for a while, but then Desi grew tired and wanted to rest. "Where's a good place to sit down?" he wondered.

Alex pointed. "On those park benches near the bike path," he said. "Let's go!" Without delay, Alex dashed over to the benches and sat down.

"Yow!" he exclaimed, and jumped up. "The benches are all wet. Now the back of my pants and shirt are soaked."

"The sun's getting warm," noticed Desi. "Maybe we can find a dry place where you can lie on your stomach in the sun to dry off. It's pretty warm now, so you should dry off quickly."

Alex thought this was a very good idea. In a bit, the two boys spotted a dry patch of grass. Alex immediately darted toward it and lay down.

"Wait," said Desi noticing a small sign at the edge of the grass. "What does that sign say?"

12

"I don't care," said Alex. "This warm sun feels good on my back, and I'm sure I'll be dry in no time."

Desi looked at the sign. It read KEEP OFF. SPRINKLERS IN USE.

Before Desi could warn Alex, the sprinklers squirted on. Alex was instantly soaked by the spray of the sprinklers. He jumped up and sprinted through the downpour to safety on the dry sidewalk.

"Now I'm wetter than ever," he moaned. "What am I going to do?"

"Maybe you should go home and put on dry clothes. You're drenched," said Desi as he looked at his dripping and **bedraggled** friend.

"That's a good idea," replied Alex. "I'm too wet to want to do anything but get dry."

It was a long walk to Alex's house, and along the way Alex's clothes began to dry out. Alex began to feel happier and happier as he became drier and drier.

The two boys strolled near a small pond just before Alex's house. The two pals often looked for minnows and frogs near the edge of this pond. "I wonder if there are any tadpoles in the pond today." said Desi.

"Should we look?" asked Alex. "I'm almost completely dry now."

The two boys headed toward the pond. A steep muddy slope led to the water's edge. They stopped.

"I've learned my lesson," said Alex. "I'm going to look before I leap this time."

"What do you mean?" asked Desi.

"I can see that the slope is steep and muddy. If I try to walk down it, I'll probably slide into the pond. I'm sick and tired of being wet. For once today, I'd like to stay dry," said Alex.

"You're right," said Desi. "I don't want to get wet and muddy either. Let's look for tadpoles another day."

Tell It in Your Words

Briefly retell the story "Alex's Soggy Day" in your own words. Tell who the characters are. Tell what happens in the story. Tell how the story ends.

_____

_____

_____

_____

_____

_____

_____

Check Your Understanding

Answer these questions to see how well you understood the realistic fiction story "Alex's Soggy Day." Circle the answers.

1. The boxes tell some things that happened in the story.

Alex sits on a wet park bench.		Alex decides not to look for tadpoles.
1	2	3

   What belongs in box 2?
   A Alex and Desi walk through the park after a rain shower.
   B Alex gets sprinkled by lawn sprinklers.
   C Alex catches minnows and frogs.
   D Desi catches tadpoles.

2. Why did Alex decide he didn't want to catch tadpoles?
   A He already had caught frogs.
   B He was too wet and bedraggled to want to catch tadpoles.
   C He was hungry and just wanted to go home.
   D He had learned his lesson and didn't want to get wet again.

3. How are Desi and Alex different?
   A Desi is impatient; Alex is patient.
   B Desi likes being dry; Alex likes being wet.
   C Desi is thoughtful; Alex is impulsive.
   D Alex is thoughtful; Desi is impulsive.

4. How does the author show that Alex is hasty?
   A Alex keeps getting wet because he doesn't think before he acts.
   B Alex always beats Desi when the two run.
   C Alex sprints out of the sprinkler area.
   D Alex jumps up after his shirt and pants get wet.

5. Based on the context of the first paragraph, what does *immensely* mean?
   A never   C a great deal
   B somewhat   D often

6. This story was written to tell you
   A how to look for minnows.
   B how a boy learned a lesson.
   C how to dry off after you get wet.
   D how friends should stick together.

7. Which of these is true?
   A Desi and Alex are brothers.
   B Desi is older than Alex.
   C Alex is older than Desi.
   D Desi and Alex are friends.

8. What problem did Alex face and solve in the story?
   A Alex learned to think before acting.
   B Alex learned how to read.
   C Alex learned how to spot tadpoles in a pond.
   D Alex learned how to make a good friend.

LESSON 3: Connections

Making Text-to-Self Connections
Lesson 1

Reread the play *The Fox and the Goat* on pages 7–9. What things in the play remind you of things in your own life? Write one or two ideas from the play. Tell how each reminds you of something in your own life. For example, have you ever had water from a well? Do you take walks in the woods?

Play	Self

Answer the following questions to tell more about the play.

1. Do you think the fox should have helped the goat out of the well? Why?

   _____

   _____

   _____

   _____

2. If you could talk to the fox, what lesson would you try to teach him?

   _____

   _____

   _____

   _____

FICTION & FICTION

Reread the realistic fiction story "Alex's Soggy Day" on pages 12–14. What things in the story remind you of things in your own life? Write one or two ideas from the story. Tell how each reminds you of something in your own life. For example, does the park remind you of a park near you?

Story	Self

Answer the following questions to tell more about the story.

1. Pretend you are Alex. What would you say if Desi asked you what the sign on the grass said? What would you do?

_____

_____

_____

_____

2. Do you think that Alex has really learned his lesson? Why or why not? Use examples from the story to support your idea.

_____

_____

_____

_____

Making Text-to-Text Connections
Lesson 1 and Lesson 2

You read the play *The Fox and the Goat* on pages 7–9. You read the realistic fiction story "Alex's Soggy Day" on pages 12–14. Answer these questions to tell about the two selections.

1. a. Think about the **characters** of the fox and Desi. What was each like? Complete the chart with words that describe the fox and then Desi.

Fox	Desi

   b. Choose the correct answer and write it on the line.

   The fox and Desi were mostly _____ . (alike/different)

2. The **dialogue** in both stories helps you know what the characters are like. Write one thing each character said that shows something about him. Then tell what you learned about the character from this dialogue.

GOAT	ALEX
Dialogue: _____	Dialogue: _____
_____	_____
_____	_____
What these words tell you about the goat:	What these words tell you about Alex:
_____	_____
_____	_____
_____	_____

FICTION & FICTION

3. What are the **problems** in each story? How are the solutions alike? How are they different?

_____

_____

_____

_____

_____

4. At the beginning of the story, the author tells you that Desi and Alex are walking through a neighborhood park after a sudden rain shower. At the beginning of the play, how do you know where the fox is? Hint: Think about **stage directions**.

_____

_____

_____

_____

5. Why could the character of the fox in the **play** *not* be a character in the **realistic fiction** story "Alex's Soggy Day"?

_____

_____

_____

_____

6. How does each story tell about the theme of *looking before you leap*?

_____

_____

_____

_____

Making Text-to-World Connections
Lesson 1 and Lesson 2

   You read a play on pages 7–9 and a realistic fiction story on pages 12–14. What things in the two selections remind you of things in the real world? For example, have you heard about someone who learned a similar lesson? Have you heard about people who acted without thinking and got into trouble? Write an idea from each story. Then tell how it reminds you of something in the world.

	Story	World
The Fox and the Goat		
"Alex's Soggy Day"		

Answer these two questions to tell more about the two selections and the world.

1. The fox wasn't watching where he was walking, and he fell down a well. Today, walkers don't usually fall down wells. What might happen to someone today who didn't pay attention to where he or she was walking?

_____

_____

_____

_____

2. Alex was lucky. He only got wet. What other things might happen to someone who was in a park and didn't read the signs?

_____

_____

_____

_____

FICTION & FICTION

Extend the Selections
Lesson 1 and Lesson 2

Now use your ideas to take the selections beyond the page!

1. Rewrite one part of "Alex's Soggy Day" as a play. Use dialogue to tell
   the story. Use stage directions to tell the actors what to do.

   _____

   _____

   _____

   _____

   _____

2. Think about the goat in *The Fox and the Goat*. What does the goat think?
   How does he feel about the fox? Write what the goat might say. Then read
   the goat's words to a classmate. Use your voice to show the goat's feelings.

   _____

   _____

   _____

   _____

3. The fox climbed up the goat's back in the play. Imagine that the goat
   climbed up the fox's back. How would the story end? Would the goat
   then help the fox out of the well? Use what you know about the goat's
   character. Write a new ending for the play.

   _____

   _____

   _____

   _____

4. On a separate sheet of paper, draw a picture of an event from each
   selection. Label your drawings.

FICTION & FICTION

UNIT 2 FICTION ⟷ FICTION

Preview

The two selections in Unit 2 are fiction.

In Lesson 4, you will read a POURQUOI TALE, "How the Rhinoceros Got His Skin."

In Lesson 5, you will read a FANTASY FICTION story, "The Day the Rhinos Flew."

The two selections in Unit 2 share the topic of <u>rhinos</u>.

In Lesson 6, you will make connections:

text to self

text to text

text to world

Fiction comes from a writer's imagination. The stories are made up. The purpose of fiction stories is to entertain. Most fiction stories have the following elements and form:

- **Setting:** The setting is when and where a story happens.

- **Characters:** The characters are the people or animals in the story.

- **Problem:** The problem is something that the characters must face and solve.

- **Plot Events:** The events are what the characters do to solve the problem. The events are the action.

- **Resolution:** The resolution is the "end" of the story.

As you read the stories in Unit 2, pay special attention to these elements: **Setting** and **Resolution**.

- **Setting:** The setting is when and where the story happens. The time of the story can be the time of day, the time of year, or the time in history. The place can be almost any place. Sometimes a story could not have happened at any other time or place.

- **Resolution:** The resolution tells how the characters solve the problem. The resolution is the "end" of the story. Many stories end with happy or fair resolutions. But sometimes an ending is sad.

Fiction stories can have certain features. As you read the selections in Unit 2, pay special attention to this feature: **Imagery**.

- **Imagery:** Imagery is language that relates to the five senses. The senses are sight, sound, smell, taste, and touch. Imagery helps you form pictures in your mind of the story events. An author may describe how something looks, sounds, smells, tastes, or feels to help you form these pictures.

LESSON 4: Pourquoi Tale, "How the Rhinoceros Got His Skin"

Get Ready to Read

Learn About Pourquoi Tales

"How the Rhinoceros Got His Skin" is a pourquoi tale.

> Pourquoi tales are stories that explain why things are the way they are. The word pourquoi (poōr KWA) means "why" in French. The characters in a pourquoi tale are often animals that speak and act like humans. These fantasy tales usually take place long ago. Many pourquoi tales have the word *why* or *how* in the title.

Think About Vocabulary

When you read this story, you may come across some new words. You may also find words used in unusual ways. Here are two words for you to know before you read.

lumbering: to move in a heavy, clumsy way
righted: placed in an upright position

As you read the story, circle at least three more words. Write the words and what they mean in the story. Use a dictionary to check each meaning.

Show What You Know

This story is about a rhinoceros. What do you know about rhinos? Where do they live? What do they look like? Use what you know to draw a sketch of a rhino.

Return to your sketch after you have read the story. Add more details if you can.

Read "How the Rhinoceros Got His Skin"

Read this **pourquoi tale** that explains how rhinos got their skin. A rhino, or rhinoceros, is a large mammal with great folds of skin on its body. It also has one or two horns on its nose.

As you read, pay attention to when and where this story take place. Also think about the ending and the use of imagery.

How the Rhinoceros Got His Skin

retelling of a story by Rudyard Kipling

A long time ago on an island in the Red Sea, there lived a woman. She lived alone on the island with nothing but her clothes, her knife, and a cooking stove. One day she mixed flour and water and raisins and plums and sugar to make a big cake. The cake was three feet wide and three feet tall. She baked it and baked it and baked it until it was a perfect golden brown.

Just as the woman was going to eat the cake, a rhinoceros came **lumbering** into the woman's camp. The rhinoceros had a horn on his nose and no manners. In those days, a rhino's skin fit tightly. It had no wrinkles anywhere.

In fear, the woman left her cake and climbed to the top of a palm tree. The rhinoceros tipped over the stove with his nose, and the cake rolled onto the sand. The rhino then spiked the cake with the horn on his nose, threw it up in the air, and ate it. Then he went away, waving his tail.

The woman came down from the tree. She **righted** the stove. Then she said, "Whoever takes a cake that I bake is making a dreadful mistake."

The next day, there was a heat wave in the Red Sea. It was so hot that everybody went to the beach to cool down. The woman went to the beach. All the animals went, too. Even the ill-mannered rhino went. The rhino was so hot that he took off his skin and carried it over his shoulder as he went down to the beach. In those days, his skin buttoned underneath him with three buttons. He said nothing to the woman about eating her cake. He headed straight for the water and blew bubbles through his nose. He left his skin on the beach.

The woman found the rhino's skin. She smiled a smile so large that it seemed to run around her face two times. Then she danced around the skin and rubbed her hands.

She went back to her camp and filled her hat with cake crumbs that the rhino had left behind. He was a sloppy eater, so there were many crumbs. She brought the crumbs back to the beach where the rhino's skin lay. Then she rubbed the skin full of old, dry, stale, tickly cake crumbs and some burned raisins. She climbed to the top of a palm tree and waited.

Soon the rhino came out of the water and put on his skin. He buttoned the three buttons. The skin tickled like cake crumbs in a bed. The rhino wanted to scratch, but that made the itching worse. He lay down on the sand and rolled and rolled and rolled. The cake crumbs only tickled him worse and worse and worse. Then he ran to the palm tree and rubbed and rubbed and rubbed. He rubbed so much that he rubbed his skin into a great fold over his shoulders. Then he rubbed another fold underneath. He rubbed off the three buttons. He rubbed more folds over his legs. But the cake crumbs didn't stop itching.

The rhino went home, very angry indeed, and terribly scratchy. From that day to this, every rhinoceros has great folds in his skin and a very bad temper.

Tell It in Your Words

Briefly retell the pourquoi tale "How the Rhinoceros Got His Skin" in your own words. Tell who the characters are. Tell what happens in the story. Tell how the story ends.

_____

_____

_____

_____

_____

_____

_____

Check Your Understanding

Answer these questions to see how well you understood the pourquoi tale "How the Rhinoceros Got His Skin." Circle the answers.

1. What is this tale mostly about?
   A a woman who bakes a very large cake
   B a place by the Red Sea where it is very hot
   C a rhinoceros who creates wrinkles in his skin
   D a camp that contains a cooking stove and cake crumbs

2. Reread the third paragraph. What does *spiked* mean?
   A threw it down   C dropped
   B crumbled   D stabbed

3. Which of the following could complete the character web of the rhinoceros?

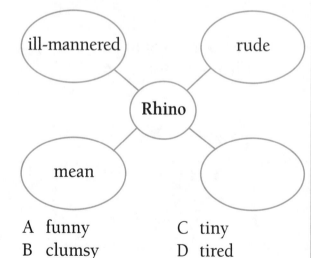

   A funny   C tiny
   B clumsy   D tired

4. Where does this story take place?
   A on an warm island
   B on a cold, snowy mountain
   C in an ocean
   D near a canyon

5. Which of these happened first?
   A There was a heat wave.
   B The woman put crumbs in the rhino's skin.
   C The rhinoceros ate a cake that didn't belong to him.
   D The rhinoceros removed his skin to go to the beach.

6. The rhinoceros got wrinkles in his skin because
   A he rolled around on the sand.
   B he rubbed against a palm tree.
   C the woman fed him too much cake.
   D the woman wrinkled his skin.

7. The author says "She smiled a smile so large that it seemed to run around her face two times." What does this mean?
   A The woman's smile was too small.
   B The woman laughed very loudly.
   C The woman's mouth was much larger than her nose or eyes.
   D The woman was very happy and had a huge smile.

8. Which of these parts of the resolution could not happen in real life?
   A A rhino rubs wrinkles into his skin.
   B A rhino rolls in the sand.
   C A rhino rubs against a palm tree.
   D A rhino is angry.

FICTION & FICTION

LESSON 5: Fantasy Fiction
"The Day the Rhinos Flew"

Get Ready to Read

Learn About Fantasy Fiction

"The Day the Rhinos Flew" is a fantasy fiction story.

> Fantasy fiction stories are about people, places, and things that could not be real. The events in fantasy fiction stories could not happen in real life. The characters are often unusual beings or creatures. For example, the characters might be unicorns, talking animals, or toys that come alive.

Think About Vocabulary

When you read this story, you may come across some new words. You may also see words used in unusual ways. Here are three words for you to know before you read.

extinct: no longer living; often used when all animals of a certain type have died out

vast: large

midst: in the middle of

As you read the story, circle at least three more words. Write the words and what they mean in the story. Use a dictionary to check each meaning.

Show What You Know

This story takes place on a grassy plain. What do you know about grassy plains? Do trees grow there? Are there hills, or is the land flat? Fill in the chart with your ideas.

If you have more ideas after you read the story, you can add to the chart.

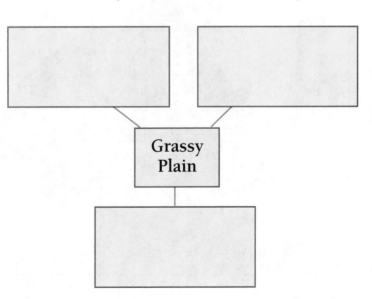

Read "The Day the Rhinos Flew"

This story is about rhinos. Think about the details that make it a **fantasy fiction** story. Also pay attention to the imagery. What pictures do you form in your mind? Think about how the story ends.

The Day the Rhinos Flew

A long time ago there were millions of rhinos. Then people began to hunt them. They killed the rhinos for their large horns. By the year 2000, only 12,000 rhinos were left on the earth. By the year 2100, only 120 were left. By the year 2200, only 12 were left.

These 12 rhinos knew they had to do something. Otherwise rhinos would soon be **extinct**. But what could they do? They'd been trying for hundreds of years to hide from humans, but the humans always found them.

One day as the rhinos were eating tall grasses on a **vast** plain, a young girl walked into their **midst**. Rhinos have terrible eyesight, so they didn't see her until she was only three feet away.

"Who are you?" yelled Raj when he noticed the girl. Raj was the oldest and wisest of the rhinos. He was almost thirty years old.

"It is only I, Mandana. I heard about your problem. I want to help," the girl said.

"You!" laughed Raj. "You are only a young girl. And what's more, you are the enemy. We could never trust you."

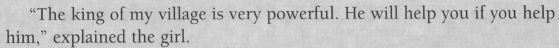

"The king of my village is very powerful. He will help you if you help him," explained the girl.

Raj snorted. "We trust no humans."

The girl continued, "I have heard stories my entire life about how good rhinos are at stamping out fires."

"True enough," Raj said. Rhinos had always been good at stamping out fires, and Raj was proud to hear that even the humans had noticed their abilities. Stamping out fires took courage and skill.

"Someone in our village started a fire," the girl said. "The weather is very dry now. If you don't help us put out the fire, it will spread. It will destroy our village. It will destroy these plains."

Raj worried. He knew the rhinos depended on the grasses of the plains for food. And when the rhinos lay down in the tall grasses, no one could see them. If the grasses burned, rhinos would have nowhere to hide from human hunters.

The rhinos looked at the sky. Even with their bad eyesight, they could see great billowing smoke clouding the sky. The plains were on fire!

"We'll help!" Raj decided.

Although rhinos are large animals, they are remarkably fast. They rushed to the edges of the fire and started stamping. They stamped and stamped and stamped. At first they only stopped the fire from advancing, but gradually they beat the fire back. By dusk the fire was out.

The rhinos were exhausted. They walked back to the tall grasses and lay down. The girl reappeared in front of them. "It's me, Mandana," she said. "I have brought the king of my village."

"What!" exclaimed Raj, on his feet at once, ready to fight.

"Have no fear," said the king. "I have come to thank you for saving my people. In return, I would like to help you."

"The only thing that could save us would be if we sprouted wings and flew to a world without people," snorted Raj.

Suddenly all 12 rhinos sprouted wings. The rhinos flapped their wings—gently at first and then harder and harder. The rhinos sailed into the sky.

"Fly into the smoke," shouted the king. "It will take you to a new world—a world with no people."

From that day on, humans never saw rhinos again. Most people thought they had become extinct. But some people believe they live happily in a world far away from humans.

Tell It in Your Words

Briefly retell the story "The Day the Rhinos Flew" in your own words. Tell who the characters are. Tell what happens in the story. Tell how the story ends.

_____

_____

_____

_____

_____

_____

_____

FICTION & FICTION

Check Your Understanding

Answer these questions to see how well you understood the fantasy fiction story "The Day the Rhinos Flew." Circle the answers.

1. What happens first in the story?
   A The rhinos rest after putting out the fire.
   B The rhinos talk to the king of the village.
   C A girl asks the rhinos for help.
   D Humans never see rhinos again.

2. Why didn't the rhinos see the girl until she was very close?
   A The girl snuck up on the rhinos.
   B Rhinos have very poor eyesight.
   C It was night time.
   D The girl was too small to worry about.

3. The author uses imagery that makes the grassy area seem
   A hilly and wet.
   B small and muddy.
   C large and flat.
   D damp and sandy.

4. In this story, the rhinos look at the sky. They see billowing smoke. What does *billowing* mean?
   A puffy
   B clear
   C light
   D hot

5. This story was written to
   A describe how rhinos live.
   B tell a fantasy about a time when rhinos flew.
   C try to get you to protect rhinos.
   D explain what life was like in Mandana's village.

6. Which of the following is a fact?
   A Rhinos will always stamp out fires if you ask them.
   B Some rhinos have wings.
   C Rhinos should never fear humans.
   D Rhinos are large animals that eat grasses.

7. At the end, what do most people think has happened to the rhinos?
   A They think rhinos live in a land without humans.
   B They think rhinos have become extinct.
   C They think rhinos live where they have always lived.
   D They think nothing has happened to the rhinos.

8. After the rhinos grew wings, what did they probably do?
   A They looked for other fires to put out.
   B They flew back to the village to show Mandana their wings.
   C They had a big party to thank the king.
   D They flew to a place without humans.

FICTION & FICTION

33

LESSON 6: Connections

Making Text-to-Self Connections
Lesson 4

   Reread the pourquoi tale "How the Rhinoceros Got His Skin" on pages 25–27. What things in the tale remind you of things in your own life? Write one or two ideas from the tale. Tell how each reminds you of something in your own life. For example, have you ever gone to a beach on a hot day? Do you get angry if someone takes something from you?

Pourquoi Tale	Self

Answer the following questions to tell more about the pourquoi tale.

1. Do you think the woman should have put crumbs in the rhino's skin? Why or why not?

   _____

   _____

   _____

   _____

2. If you lived on the island, what would you do if the rhino stole your cake?

   _____

   _____

   _____

   _____

Making Text-to-Self Connections
Lesson 5

Reread the fantasy fiction story "The Day the Rhinos Flew" on pages 30–32. What things in the story remind you of things in your own life? Write one or two ideas from the story. Tell how each reminds you of something in your own life. For example, have you ever seen smoke from a fire?

Story	Self

Answer the following questions to tell more about the story.

3. Do you think the rhinos were smart to want to live in a world without people? Why?

_____

_____

_____

_____

4. If you could fly, where would you go and what would you do?

_____

_____

_____

_____

_____

Making Text-to-Text Connections
Lesson 4 and Lesson 5

You read the pourquoi tale "How the Rhinoceros Got His Skin" on pages 25–27. You read the fantasy fiction story "The Day the Rhinos Flew" on pages 30–32. Answer these questions to tell about the two selections.

1. Part of the **setting** is the place that the story happens.

   a. Describe the place where the rhinos live in these two stories.

   "How the Rhinoceros Got His Skin": _____

   _____

   "The Day the Rhinos Flew": _____

   _____

   b. How do you think the two places might be alike? _____

   _____

2. Finish the chart. List one or two words or phrases from each story that help you see, feel, hear, smell, or taste what is happening. These are examples of **imagery**. After each example, write which of the five senses the example describes. Two answers are given.

"How the Rhinoceros Got His Skin"	"The Day the Rhinos Flew"
golden brown, sight	*Raj snorted, hearing*

3. Describe the **resolution**, or ending, of each story. Use words that describe your feelings about each ending, such as *happy, sad, funny, fair,* and so on. Then tell why the ending is like that.

a. "How the Rhinoceros Got His Skin"

The ending is _____ because _____

_____ .

b. "The Day the Rhinos Flew"

The ending is _____ because _____

_____ .

4. Could both of these stories be called **fantasy fiction** stories? Could both be called **pourquoi tales**? Explain your ideas.

_____

_____

_____

_____

_____

5. What is one idea about *rhinos* that you learn from both stories?

_____

_____

_____

6. What did the *rhinos* in these stories do that real rhinos are not able to do?

_____

_____

_____

_____

Making Text-to-World Connections
Lesson 4 and Lesson 5

You read a pourquoi tale on pages 25–27 and a fantasy fiction story on pages 30–32. What things in the two selections remind you of things in the real world? Have you heard about a heat wave? Do you know someone who had something stolen? Have you heard about animals that are near extinction? Write an idea from each story. Then tell how it reminds you of something in the world.

	Story	World
"How the Rhinoceros Got His Skin"		
"The Day the Rhinos Flew"		

Answer these two questions to tell more about the two stories and the world.

1. What are rhinos really like? List some ways that real rhinos are like the rhinos in the two stories.

_____

_____

_____

_____

2. Imagine that one of these stories is a current news story. What would the headline be? Write it. Then write the first paragraph of the news story.

_____

_____

_____

_____

FICTION & FICTION

Extend the Selections
Lesson 4 and Lesson 5

Now use your ideas to take the selections beyond the page!

1. In the pourquoi tale, the rhino steals the woman's cake. Then the woman puts crumbs under the rhino's skin. Do you think this fight will continue? What could you say to the two characters to get them to stop fighting? Write your ideas.

_____

_____

_____

_____

2. What is the rhino thinking in "How the Rhinoceros Got His Skin"? Write dialogue that tells what he is thinking when he puts on the scratchy skin.

_____

_____

_____

_____

3. Imagine that one of these stories takes place in a very different setting— in a jungle, a swamp, on top of a snowy mountain, or in outer space, for example. How would the story change with the new setting? Write notes here. Then tell the new story to a partner.

_____

_____

_____

_____

4. On a separate sheet of paper, draw a picture of your idea of the rhinos flying away in "The Day the Rhinos Flew."

Preview

The two selections in Unit 3 are nonfiction.

In Lesson 7, you will read an INFORMATIONAL ARTICLE, "Orphan Trains."

In Lesson 8, you will read DIARY ENTRIES, "The Difficult Journey."

The two selections in Unit 3 share the topic of <u>orphan trains</u>.

In Lesson 9, you will explore connections:

text to self

text to text

text to world

Nonfiction tells about things that are real. The purpose of nonfiction selections is to inform or record. Most nonfiction selections have the following elements and form:

- **Introduction:** This is the beginning. It tells the topic, or what the selection is about. It includes some information to grab your interest and make you want to keep reading. Some nonfiction selections may have something like a **setting**. This is when and where events take place.

- **Body:** This is the middle. It tells more about the topic. It gives important points, or **main ideas**, about the topic. It also gives **details** to support the main ideas. The ideas are organized in a way that makes sense for the topic.

- **Conclusion:** This is the ending of the selection. The conclusion summarizes the important ideas. It brings the selection to a satisfying close.

Nonfiction selections can include various **features**. As you read the selections in Unit 3, pay special attention to these features: **Setting**, **Sequence**, and **Imagery**.

- **Setting:** Some nonfiction selections have a specific setting, like fiction stories have. The events take place in a specific time and place. Often, the events couldn't have taken place in any other time and place. For example, journal or diary entries written by someone during the American Revolution would have something to do with that time and place. The entries would record the writer's own experiences. But the experiences would be "set" within the American Revolution.

- **Sequence:** Sequence is the order in which events happen. Noticing the order will help you to see how events lead into each other.

- **Imagery:** Writers create imagery by making you think of your five senses: taste, touch, smell, sight, and hearing. The mental pictures that you form help you understand and "see" in your mind what you have read. Imagery helps you share the writer's ideas and feelings.

NONFICTION & NONFICTION

LESSON 7: Informational Article "Orphan Trains"

Get Ready to Read

Learn About Informational Articles

"Orphan Trains" is an informational article.

> An informational article gives information about a topic. The beginning draws readers in. The article might have a specific setting. Facts and examples make up the middle, or body, of the article. The ending sums up the ideas in the article.

Think About Vocabulary

When you read this article, you may come across some new words. You may also find words used in unusual ways. Here are two words for you to know before you read.

orphanages: places where children without parents or others to take care of them were sent to live

orphan: a child without a mother or father or anyone else to take care of him or her

As you read the article, circle at least three more words. Write the words and what they mean in the article. Use a dictionary to check each meaning.

Show What You Know

This article is about orphan trains in the 1850s. What do you imagine life was like for children then? Compare that with what life is like for children today. Write your ideas in the chart.

1850s	Today

You can add to the chart after you read the article.

Read "Orphan Trains"

Read this **informational article** about the life of some children in the 1850s. As you read, think about how life is different for children today. Notice when and where the events take place. Pay attention to the sequence of events. Be aware of how the imagery makes you feel. Does it make you happy? Sad?

Orphan Trains

In the 1800s and early 1900s, thousands of men and women came to the United States. They came from other countries. They wanted to find a better life. Most of these people were poor. Many did not speak English.

However, life in America was not easy. There were not enough jobs for all the newcomers. Those that did find jobs worked long hours. They did not get paid much. They did not get paid at all if they were sick. If they got hurt on the job, tough luck. Someone else could replace them.

Many of these families suffered terribly. Families did not eat well. They shivered in the winter. They melted in the summer. The apartments they lived in were old and overcrowded. Illnesses spread easily in these places. Few people had enough money to see a doctor. The death rate was high.

Children in these families often led difficult lives. Sometimes a mother or father (or both) died. Sometimes the parents could no longer afford to take care of the children. Some children were sent to **orphanages**. Others lived on the streets.

NONFICTION & NONFICTION

43

In 1854, there were 34,000 homeless children in New York City. These children sold matches, rags, or newspapers. They begged. They stole food. Some children banded together. They formed gangs. Police started putting these children in jail. Some were only five years old.

One man, Charles Loring Brace, decided to help these children. He said, "When a child of the streets stands before you in rags, with a tear-stained face, you cannot easily forget him." But what could Brace do? There were not enough orphanages to take in all the homeless children.

Brace had an idea. Why not send these children to live on farms in the west? He thought farmers might take in the homeless children. He hoped farmers would treat the children well.

Brace sent out notices to towns in the Midwest. The notices said that trains full of children were coming. The children were from orphanages in New York. These children needed a good home. The notices also said that people taking in the children had to treat them like members of the family. They had to send the children to school. They had to properly feed and clothe them.

Then the trains started coming. **Orphan** trains ran from 1854 until 1929. More than 100,000 children

rode the orphan trains. At each town along the route, the children got out. They lined up in front of a crowd of people. The people examined the children. They looked at the children's teeth. They felt their muscles. Some people wanted a boy to work on the farm. Others wanted a girl to help with household chores. Some felt sorry for the children and just wanted to give them a good home.

After a child was selected, he or she left with the family. The children who were not selected got back on the train. They went to the next stop. The process continued. Finally all the children had new homes.

NONFICTION & NONFICTION

Some children found better homes than others. A few families were not kind. Some children had to work long hours. Others weren't fed enough. Still others were ignored or treated badly.

However, there were far more happy endings than sad endings. Many children found good homes. They no longer had to worry about finding food. They had a warm house to live in and warm clothes to wear. They went to school, and their future held promise.

Tell It in Your Words

Briefly summarize the informational article "Orphan Trains" in your own words. Tell the most important ideas and any important details.

_____

_____

_____

_____

_____

_____

_____

_____

Check Your Understanding

Answer these questions to see how well you understood the informational article "Orphan Trains." Circle the answers.

1. What is this article mostly about?
   A life for children in New York City
   B farm life in the 1800s
   C workers of the 1800s
   D what orphan trains were like

2. The article says "Brace sent out notices to towns in the Midwest." In this sentence, the word *notices* means
   A sees   C reporters
   B announcements   D children

3. When did orphan trains begin running?
   A the early 1800s
   B 1929
   C 1854
   D the early 1900s

4. The boxes tell about the order of events in the article.

People were told that trains full of children were coming.		Each child found a new family.
1	2	3

   What belongs in box 2?
   A The children arrived by train.
   B Many newcomers arrived in New York City.
   C Charles Brace wanted to help homeless children.
   D The orphan trains stopped running.

5. Brace began running orphan trains
   A to help farmers leave the Midwest.
   B to build more orphanages.
   C to help homeless children.
   D to help the railroads.

6. What would probably have happened if the orphan trains had not run?
   A Families in New York would have taken in the homeless children.
   B More homeless children would have lived on New York streets.
   C More orphanages would have been quickly built.
   D More children would have attended school.

7. Which of these is an opinion?
   A The Midwest was the best place to live.
   B More than 100,000 children rode orphan trains.
   C Orphan trains stopped running in 1929.
   D In 1854, there were 34,000 homeless children in New York.

8. Which statement could sum up or conclude the selection?
   A Most orphan train riders did not find good homes.
   B The children hated the trains.
   C Most people wanted boys to work on farms.
   D Most children found good homes.

LESSON 8: Diary Entries
"The Difficult Journey"

Get Ready to Read

Learn About Diary Entries

"The Difficult Journey" is a series of diary entries.

> A diary entry is written by someone in a diary, or log. In the entry, the writer tells about his or her life. The entry might include events, experiences, thoughts, or ideas. Entries are often dated. They may be long or short.

Think About Vocabulary

When you read these diary entries, you may come across some new words. You may also see words used in unusual ways. Here are three words for you to know before you read.

distressful: causing suffering or fear
incorrigible: difficult or impossible to control
schoolteacher: someone who teaches in a school

As you read the diary entries, circle at least three more words. Write the words and what they mean in the diary. Use a dictionary to check each meaning.

Show What You Know

The girl who writes this diary is an orphan. What kinds of problems might a child without parents write about? Write your ideas in the box.

Problems

You can add ideas to the box after you read the diary entries.

Read "The Difficult Journey"

This selection is adapted from several children's descriptions of their experiences with orphan trains. These **diary entries** are what one girl might have told about her life before, during, and after a ride on an orphan train. When you read, think about the setting. Could these events have happened at any other time or place? Pay attention to the dates so that you can tell how long it is between events. Also think about the images that come to your mind as you read.

The Difficult Journey

April 7, 1854 My father died when I was young. I am very close to my mother. We have no one else. We only have each other. My mother has had stabbing headaches for a long time. Last month she went to a hospital to have tests taken. That was the last time I saw her.

May 12 I like to sing, so now I am a singing girl. I go on boats and sing. Sometimes people pay me. There is no other way for me to get along. Some people say I have a good voice. Singing keeps the **distressful** thoughts away.

At night I live with other homeless girls. We sneak into a basement. We are always hungry. We sleep on the floor. Rats run over our hair at night, and we wake up screaming. I wish I knew where my mother was.

June 31 I have gone to live in an orphanage. I am lucky. Most orphanages do not have room for even one more person. But I think they felt sorry for me. Now at least I have a bed and food and baths.

August 5 Today many of us in the orphanage got scratchy, new clothes. We must get up early tomorrow to ride a train. We are going to find new homes far from New York City. I don't want to leave my friends behind. What has happened to my mother? I'm afraid about my future.

August 10 We have been riding this train for three and a half days. We eat and sleep in our seats. Now we have to put on our new clothes, brush our hair, and wash our face. We are almost there.

August 11 Yesterday we all got off the train. They lined us up. People pulled and shoved me. They ran their dirty fingers over my teeth. I felt like biting them, but I didn't.

One man came up to me and said, "My wife needs a girl like you to help on our farm."

I said, "I won't go with you. You smell. You probably haven't had a bath in a month."

The man took my arm. He dragged me away. I bit him as hard as I could. He kept dragging me, so I kicked him until he let go. All of the other people thought I was **incorrigible**. No one wanted me after that. I sat in a chair and cried.

Then a **schoolteacher** came up to me. She said, "I will take you home with me. I will try to find a family for you."

She talked to her friends. An old man and woman came to see me. They didn't have any children. The man said to me, "If you come with us, we will send you to school. We will get you a puppy and a pony."

I didn't know what to do, but they seemed nice, so I said, "Yes, I will come."

August 12 I am in my new home. My new parents are nice to me, but I miss my mother terribly. I am afraid I will never see her again.

My new parents live on a farm with sheep and chickens and cows. They gave me a fuzzy black puppy. I feel rich. No girls in New York own puppies.

September 12 I went to school today. I think I would like to be a schoolteacher when I grow up. The teacher is so nice. The other children are not very friendly, however. They avoid me because I am an orphan.

Oh, what a difficult journey my life has been so far. I wonder what my future holds.

Tell It in Your Words

Briefly summarize the diary entries "The Difficult Journey" in your own words. Tell about the most important events.

_____

_____

_____

_____

_____

_____

_____

_____

Check Your Understanding

Answer these questions to see how well you understood the diary entries "The Difficult Journey." Circle the answers.

1. The boxes tell some things that happened in the diary entries.

The girl becomes a singing girl.	The girl goes to an orphanage.	
1	2	3

   What belongs in box 3?
   A The girl's mother goes to a hospital.
   B The girl rides on an orphan train.
   C The girl's father dies.
   D The girl sleeps in basements with other homeless girls.

2. The girl writes mostly about
   A her life as a singing girl.
   B her life in the orphanage.
   C her life shortly after her mother dies.
   D family life with her mother.

3. Which of these was not mentioned?
   A The girl's mother died at a hospital.
   B The girl got a puppy.
   C The girl's father died when she was young.
   D The girl got new clothes at the orphanage.

4. How can you tell that this is a diary and not another kind of writing?
   A There are interesting characters.
   B The writing contains dialogue.
   C The writing contains facts.
   D Each entry is dated.

5. You can tell from the entries that
   A the girl will become a teacher.
   B being homeless was easier in the 1800s than it is today.
   C the girl had many misfortunes.
   D all children had to attend school in the 1800s.

6. What did the girl mean when she said, "There is no other way for me to get along?"
   A Singing was the only way the girl could make her friends happy.
   B The girl knew of no other way to stay alive.
   C The girl had no other way of traveling to the Midwest.
   D Singing girls make new friends.

7. Before going to the orphanage, the girl often slept
   A on a train.
   B in a warm bed.
   C at friends' houses.
   D in basements.

8. The girl writes, "Rats run over our hair at night." This image relates mostly to the sense of
   A touch.
   B sound.
   C smell.
   D taste.

LESSON 9: Connections

Making Text-to-Self Connections
Lesson 7

Reread the informational article "Orphan Trains" on pages 43–45. What things in the article remind you of things in your own life? Write one or two ideas from the article. Tell how each reminds you of something in your own life. For example, have you ever visited a city? Have you ridden on a train?

Informational Article	Self

Answer the following questions to tell more about the article.

1. Do you think Charles Loring Brace should have sent children away on trains? Why or why not?

   _____

   _____

   _____

   _____

2. If you were Brace, what else would you do to help homeless children?

   _____

   _____

   _____

   _____

NONFICTION & NONFICTION

Making Text-to-Self Connections
Lesson 8

Reread the diary entries "The Difficult Journey" on pages 48–50. What things in the diary entries remind you of things in your own life? Write one or two ideas from the diary entries. Tell how each reminds you of something in your own life. For example, do you dislike rats?

Diary Entries	Self

Answer the following questions to tell more about the diary entries.

1. Imagine you are the diary writer. What is one reason you would want to go on an orphan train? What is one reason you would not want to go? Write the reasons.

_____

_____

_____

_____

2. The girl doesn't seem to feel sorry for herself even though she faced hardships. How do you think she stayed hopeful about her future?

_____

_____

_____

_____

Making Text-to-Text Connections
Lesson 7 and Lesson 8

You read the informational article "Orphan Trains" on pages 43–45. You read the diary entries "The Difficult Journey" on pages 48–50. Answer these questions to tell about the two selections.

1. Think about the **setting** in both selections. How are the settings in both selections alike?

   _____

   _____

   _____

2. Think about the **imagery** in the selections. Find words or phrases in both that relate to one of the five senses. List the examples. Beside each example, write one sense that it relates to. Two answers are given.

"Orphan Trains"	"The Difficult Journey"
shivered, touch	*scratchy, touch*

3. Do you think Charles Loring Brace would have continued the *orphan trains* if he knew the way that many of the children were treated when they got off the trains? Why or why not?

   _____

   _____

   _____

NONFICTION & NONFICTION

4. The **sequence** in both selections helps you know how one event leads to another. Below are events that happened in the selections. After each event, tell what happened next.

a. Charles Loring Brace saw homeless children on the streets of New York.

He wanted to help these children, so _____

_____

b. The mother of the girl disappeared. The girl then _____

_____

5. Fill in the diagram. In the left section, tell another way that the **informational article** is different from the **diary entries**. In the right section, tell another way that the diary entries are different from the informational article. The center section tells how the two are the same.

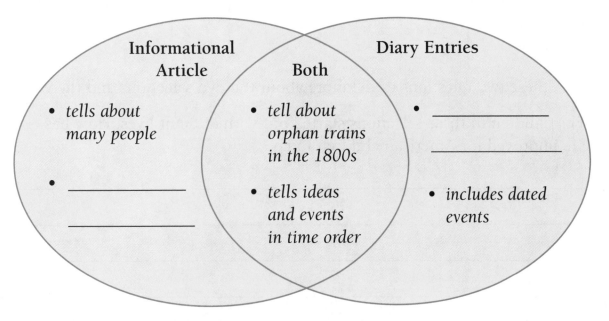

Informational Article

- *tells about many people*

- _____

_____

Both

- *tell about orphan trains in the 1800s*

- *tells ideas and events in time order*

Diary Entries

- _____

_____

- *includes dated events*

6. Charles Loring Brace started the *orphan trains* because he had a view of the future for orphans. How was his view different from the view of the girl who wrote the diary when she was in New York? Did the view of the girl change once she was in her new home in the Midwest?

_____

_____

_____

Making Text-to-World Connections
Lesson 7 and Lesson 8

You read an informational article on pages 43–45 and a series of diary entries on pages 48–50. What things in the two selections remind you of things in the real world? Do you know about someone who has faced hardships? Has someone in your family come to the United States from another country? Write an idea from each selection. Then tell how it reminds you of something in the world.

	Selection	World
"Orphan Trains"		
"The Difficult Journey"		

Answer these two questions to tell more about the two selections and the world.

1. The children in these selections started out with difficult lives. How has life improved for American children today?

   _____

   _____

   _____

   _____

2. The United States has always had newcomers. Why is life often harder for newcomers than for those who have been here longer?

   _____

   _____

   _____

   _____

NONFICTION & NONFICTION

Extend the Selections
Lesson 7 and Lesson 8

Now use your ideas to take the selections beyond the page!

1. Imagine that the diary continues. What happens to the girl?
   What does she do with her life? Write more entries.

   _____

   _____

   _____

   _____

2. Think about the girl's mother in the diary entries. What would she want
   to say to her daughter? Write a note from the mother to her daughter.

   _____

   _____

   _____

   _____

3. If each selection was made into a movie, who would play the diary writer?
   Who would play Charles Loring Brace? Tell why you chose these actors.

   _____

   _____

   _____

   _____

4. On a separate sheet of paper, draw a scene from one of the selections.
   Label your drawing.

NONFICTION & NONFICTION

Preview

The two selections in Unit 4 are nonfiction. In Lesson 10, you will read a BOOK REVIEW, "Good Work, Ben."

In Lesson 11, you will read an INTERVIEW, "How Shocking, Ben Franklin."

The two selections in Unit 4 share the topic of <u>Benjamin Franklin</u>.

In Lesson 12, you will make connections:

text to self

text to text

text to world

Nonfiction tells about things that are real. Most nonfiction selections have the following elements and form:

- **Introduction:** The introduction, or beginning, tells the topic of the selection. It includes information to grab your interest and make you want to keep reading.

- **Body:** The body, or middle, tells more about the topic. It gives **main ideas**, or important points about the topic. It gives **details** that tell more about each main idea. The details are usually facts or examples.

- **Conclusion:** The conclusion is the ending of the selection. The conclusion summarizes the important ideas in the selection. It brings the selection to a satisfying close.

As you read the selections in Unit 4, pay special attention to these elements: **Main Ideas and Details**.

- **Main Ideas and Details:** The main idea of a whole selection is what that selection is all about. The main idea of a paragraph in a selection tells what that paragraph is all about. Supporting details tell more about each main idea.

Nonfiction selections may have different features. As you read the selections in Unit 4, pay special attention to these features:

- **Cause and Effect:** The cause is *why something happens*. The effect is *what happens*. Understanding causes and effects can help you see how the ideas are connected in a selection.

- **Facts and Opinions: Facts** are statements that can be proved. They are true. This sentence is a fact: *Benjamin Franklin was born in 1706.* You can look in many books to check when Franklin was born. **Opinions** are someone's ideas, thoughts, or feelings. They cannot be proved true. Look at this statement: *Benjamin Franklin was the hardest-working man in Philadelphia.* This is an opinion. Someone might believe that others worked harder. Different people have different beliefs about what *hardest-working* means. So you cannot prove the statement to be true or false.

LESSON 10: Book Review
"Good Work, Ben"

Get Ready to Read

Learn About Book Reviews

"Good Work, Ben" is a book review.

> A book review tells about a specific book. In a book review, the title of the book being reviewed and the name of the book's author are given at the beginning. The reviewer of the book then retells, or sums up, the book. There may be some quotations from the book. The end often includes the reviewer's opinion of the book. A book review may have its own title.

Think About Vocabulary

When you read this book review, you may come across some new words. You may also find words used in unusual ways. Here are three words for you to know before you read.

apprentice: someone who learns a trade by working for someone already in the trade

vain: overly proud

prose: ordinary writing that includes complete sentences and punctuation

As you read the book review, circle at least three more words. Write the words and what they mean in the review. Use a dictionary to check each meaning.

Show What You Know

This selection is a book review of a biography of Benjamin Franklin. Benjamin Franklin was very famous in the late 1700s. What do you already know about Benjamin Franklin? Write what you know in the box.

After you read the book review, you may want to add to the box.

Benjamin Franklin

Read "Good Work, Ben"

This is a **book review** of a book about Benjamin Franklin, *What's the Big Idea, Ben Franklin?* Franklin invented many useful things. He also wrote books and helped our nation win its independence from England.

As you read, pay attention to the main ideas and details. Also pay attention to the reviewer's opinion of the book.

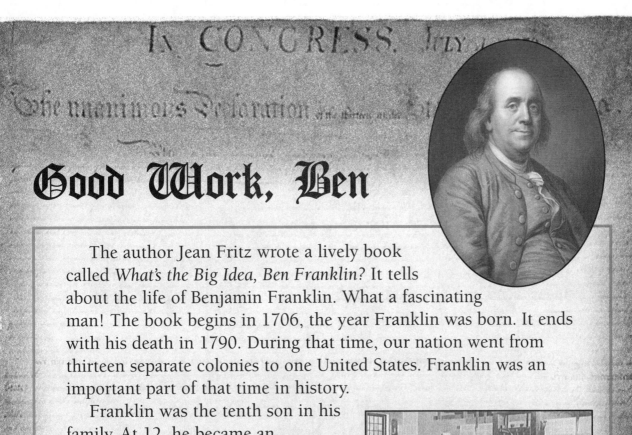

Good Work, Ben

The author Jean Fritz wrote a lively book called *What's the Big Idea, Ben Franklin?* It tells about the life of Benjamin Franklin. What a fascinating man! The book begins in 1706, the year Franklin was born. It ends with his death in 1790. During that time, our nation went from thirteen separate colonies to one United States. Franklin was an important part of that time in history.

Franklin was the tenth son in his family. At 12, he became an **apprentice**. He worked in a print shop. Benjamin had to promise to obey his master for nine years. Ben wanted to learn the printing trade. But he didn't like being bossed around. So at 17, Ben ran away. He took a boat to Philadelphia, Pennsylvania.

Ben soon owned his own print shop. And he was full of good ideas. He started the first library in America. He started Philadelphia's fire department and a hospital. He thought of ways to light streets and get rid of garbage. He helped mail move faster between cities. He was busy inventing, too. He invented a stove. He invented the lightning rod. He proved that electricity and lightning were the same. Franklin's work with electricity made him famous.

Ben was good at talking people into doing things. So he was sent to London. His job was to help America. Franklin was 51. He lived in England for 18 years. But in 1774, Ben could stand it no longer. England would not listen to him. It was treating America poorly. Ben was angry. He left England. By the time he got back, America and England were at war.

Franklin helped write the Declaration of Independence. In this document, the United States said it was free from England's rule. Later Franklin helped write the U.S. Constitution. According to Fritz, Franklin had big ideas of his own. And he played a "large part in one of the Biggest Ideas of his time—the idea of an independent United States."

The author does a great job of describing Ben Franklin. Readers learn that Franklin was stubborn and independent and curious. He may also have been **vain** and sometimes lazy. He liked to figure out how to make work and life easier. Franklin liked to have a good time. He liked to talk. And he was very friendly.

In this book, the author shows how the young Ben Franklin tried to improve himself. And the things he did were not easy. For example, to improve his writing, Ben would read an essay. Then he would rewrite it as a poem. Then, a few weeks later, he would rewrite the poem as **prose**.

Franklin also liked to read. He read books on arithmetic, how to argue, and how to be good. But he liked just about any subject. He even read books on how to catch eels and how to keep horses from having nightmares!

Jean Fritz's book makes me wish I had known Ben Franklin. Ben as a boy would have been fun to play with. He was full of ideas. But he wasn't just a dreamer. He found uses for his ideas.

As a man, Franklin watched thirteen little colonies become one nation. Some of his ideas are in our nation's most important documents. If you would like to learn about the life of a fascinating fellow, you should read *What's the Big Idea, Ben Franklin?*

—*Review by Devon Allen*

Tell It in Your Words

Briefly summarize the book review "Good Work, Ben" in your own words. Give the title of the book and the name of the author. Briefly tell what the book is about. Tell the reviewer's opinion of the book.

_____

_____

_____

_____

_____

_____

_____

Check Your Understanding

Answer these questions to see how well you understood the book review "Good Work, Ben." Circle the answers.

1. Who wrote this book review?
   A Ben Franklin
   B Devon Allen
   C Jean Fritz
   D It is impossible to know.

2. From the review, which of these is the main idea of the book?
   A Ben Franklin was born in 1706.
   B Ben Franklin ran away.
   C Ben Franklin was good at talking people into doing things.
   D Ben Franklin did many different things during his life.

3. Which of the following could complete the character web of Benjamin Franklin?

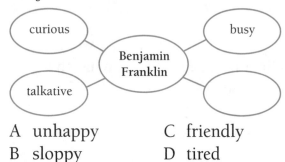

   A unhappy   C friendly
   B sloppy   D tired

4. Why did the author write the book review?
   A to summarize the book *What's the Big Idea, Ben Franklin?*
   B to show what life was like in the 1700s
   C to convince people to become inventors
   D to persuade readers to buy other books by Jean Fritz

5. Which of these happened first in the book?
   A Franklin invented a stove.
   B Franklin started a fire department.
   C Franklin was an apprentice.
   D Franklin went to London.

6. How many quotations from the book are in the book review?
   A three
   B two
   C one
   D none

7. If Franklin had not learned the printing trade, he probably would not have
   A become interested in electricity.
   B started a hospital.
   C gone to London.
   D owned a print shop.

8. What is the reviewer's opinion of this book?
   A He doesn't like the book.
   B He thinks the author describes Franklin poorly.
   C He is glad he never met Franklin.
   D He thinks others should read the book.

NONFICTION & NONFICTION

Get Ready to Read

Learn About Interviews

"How Shocking, Ben Franklin" is an interview.

> An interview is like a conversation. It is a dialogue between two people. One person asks questions. The other person answers the questions. In the introduction, the two people are named. In the body, the questions and answers are given. The conclusion is often a final question and answer. Sometimes the two people thank each other.

Think About Vocabulary

When you read this interview, you may come across some new words. You may also see words used in unusual ways. Here are three words for you to know in advance.

feat: a great task or an amazing deed
unconscious: not aware of anything
attract: cause to come together

As you read the interview, circle at least three more words. Write the words and what they mean in the interview. Use a dictionary to check each meaning.

Show What You Know

This interview takes place in the year 1787. What do people know today that they didn't know in 1787? Write your ideas in the chart.

1787	Today

You can add to the chart after you read the interview.

NONFICTION & NONFICTION

This is an **interview** with Benjamin Franklin. The questions are mostly about Franklin's greatest discovery. Pay attention to the details about the discovery. Also notice the opinions that Franklin expresses in his answers.

How Shocking, Ben Franklin
by Inez Sandoval

I am a time-traveling reporter. I have been sent back to the year 1787. I am about to interview the great inventor Benjamin Franklin. I am in Mr. Franklin's home. He seems eager to tell me about his biggest discovery.

Inez: Mr. Franklin, you've done many things in your life. What was your greatest **feat**?

Mr. Franklin: It was when I proved that lightning and electricity are the same thing. Many people thought I was crazy.

Inez: How did you become interested in electricity?

Mr. Franklin: People around the world were interested in electricity. It was a fad. In Europe, people met in dark rooms to see sparks and other tricks. Performers traveled from town to town. They put on electrical shows. It was like a circus act. I wanted to do electrical tricks, too.

Inez: Weren't you afraid of getting hurt?

Mr. Franklin: No. Perhaps I should have been. But I wasn't afraid. I wanted to see what would happen. I almost killed myself once, though.

NONFICTION & NONFICTION

66

Inez: What happened?

Mr. Franklin: I meant to use an electric shock to kill a turkey for holiday dinner. Then I planned to roast it on a fire using electricity. However, instead of shocking the turkey, I shocked myself. There was a great flash and a crack like lightning. I was knocked **unconscious**.

Inez: How did you show that electricity and lightning are the same? Lightning is up in the sky. People can't touch it.

Mr. Franklin: True. But I knew that iron rods **attract** electricity. I thought iron rods would attract lightning too. I wanted to stick an iron rod on top of a hill close to lightning. But there weren't any hills around. So I put a long pointed wire on the end of a kite. My son flew the kite during a storm.

Inez: Wasn't that dangerous?

Mr. Franklin: Yes, indeed. But I was curious. I wanted to find out.

Inez: How did you make your kite?

Mr. Franklin: I used silk and two crossed sticks for the body. At the top of the kite, I put the wire. On the string of the kite I attached a key.

Inez: Then what happened?

Mr. Franklin: My son flew the kite. Lightning hit the wire on top. I touched the key on the string, and I felt a shock. After that, I knew that electricity and lightning are the same.

Inez: How did people respond to your discovery?

Mr. Franklin: I was surprised by their reaction. This discovery made me famous. I was the most famous man in America. The King of France praised me. I received medals and honors from all over the world. But I decided I needed to put my idea to good use.

Inez: How did you do that?

Mr. Franklin: I made a lightning rod. It is a pointed iron rod that goes on the roof of a house. The rod attracts lightning. Lightning hits the rod instead of the house. The electricity travels from the rod through a wire into the ground. A house with a lightning rod will not be burned down if lightning hits it.

Inez: Thank you for your time, Mr. Franklin. Perhaps I can ask you about a different feat another day?

Mr. Franklin: Thank you for coming. You are welcome back any time.

Tell It in Your Words

Briefly summarize the interview "How Shocking, Ben Franklin" in your own words. Tell the most important ideas and any important details.

_____

_____

_____

_____

_____

_____

_____

Check Your Understanding

Answer these questions to see how well you understood the interview "How Shocking, Ben Franklin." Circle the answers.

1. What was Franklin's greatest feat?
   A creating a kite from string and two crossed sticks
   B flying a kite during a thunderstorm
   C inventing the lightning rod
   D proving that electricity and lightning are the same

2. The boxes tell about some events that are mentioned in the interview.

Franklin wants to prove that electricity and lightning are the same.		Franklin invents the lightning rod.
1	2	3

   What belongs in box 2?
   A Franklin wants to do electrical tricks.
   B Franklin is knocked unconscious.
   C Franklin feels a shock when a kite is hit by lightning.
   D Franklin becomes famous.

3. What makes this an interview and not another kind of writing?
   A Two people are named in the selection.
   B Two people have a conversation.
   C One person describes his feats.
   D One person asks questions and another person answers.

4. Who asks the questions in this interview?
   A an unnamed reporter
   B Mr. Franklin
   C Inez Sandoval
   D Devon Allen

5. What does *fad* mean?
   A the latest thing
   B a daydream
   C a new contest
   D a traveling circus

6. What is the purpose of the interview?
   A to make readers want to be like Franklin
   B to describe Franklin's greatest feat
   C to persuade readers to fly kites
   D to show how a lightning rod works

7. Which of these is an opinion?
   A Franklin received medals.
   B Franklin invented the lightning rod.
   C Franklin liked fame too much.
   D Franklin shocked himself during one experiment.

8. From this interview, you can tell that
   A Franklin did not get along well with his son.
   B Franklin's curiosity was stronger than his fears.
   C Franklin liked storms.
   D Franklin was an excellent poet.

LESSON 12: Connections

Making Text-to-Self Connections
Lesson 10

Reread the book review "Good Work, Ben" on pages 61–63. What things in the book review remind you of things in your own life? Write one or two ideas from the book review. Tell how each reminds you of something in your own life. For example, do you have a favorite book about a person's life? Have you ever written a book report or book review?

Book Review	Self

Answer the following questions to tell more about the book review.

1. Would you like to read the book *What's the Big Idea, Ben Franklin*? Why or why not?

   _____

   _____

   _____

   _____

2. What part of Franklin's life did you like learning about the most? Tell why.

   _____

   _____

   _____

   _____

Making Text-to-Self Connections
Lesson 11

Reread the interview "How Shocking, Ben Franklin" on pages 66–68. What things in the interview remind you of things in your own life? Write one or two ideas from the interview. Tell how each reminds you of something in your own life. For example, do you like fads? Have you ever done something that made other people notice you?

Interview	Self

Answer the following questions to tell more about the interview.

1. If you could interview Benjamin Franklin, what would you ask him? Why?

_____

_____

_____

_____

2. What qualities do you most admire about Benjamin Franklin? Can you improve these qualities in your life?

_____

_____

_____

_____

Making Text-to-Text Connections
Lesson 10 and Lesson 11

You read the book review "Good Work, Ben" on pages 61–63.
You read the interview "How Shocking, Ben Franklin" on pages 66–68.
Answer these questions to tell about the two selections.

1. Read the sentences below. Circle the word to tell whether each sentence is a **fact** or an **opinion**. Then tell why.

   a. Franklin was the tenth son in his family.   Fact   Opinion

   _____

   b. Franklin helped write the Declaration of Independence.   Fact   Opinion

   _____

   c. The boy Ben would have been fun to play with.   Fact   Opinion

   _____

   d. Franklin received medals and honors from all over the world. Fact   Opinion

   _____

   e. Franklin was a fascinating man!   Fact   Opinion

   _____

2. Finish the chart. List the **main idea** of a paragraph from one of the selections. Below the main idea list **details** about the main idea.

   Selection: _____

   Main Idea: _____

   _____

   Details: _____

   _____

   _____

   _____

NONFICTION & NONFICTION

3. Think about **cause and effect** events. Listed below is an event, or cause, from each selection. Tell the effect of each cause.

   a. As an apprentice, Franklin did not like to be bossed around. Because of this, he

   _____

   _____ .

   b. Franklin wanted to put his discovery about lightning and electricity to good

   use. So he _____

   _____ .

4. Fill in the chart. Show how the **book review** and the **interview** are different.

Book Review	Interview
• *about a book*	• *about Franklin's views*
• _____	• *contains dialogue*
• _____	• _____
• *gives reviewer's opinions*	• _____

5. What did you learn about *Benjamin Franklin* in these two selections?

   _____

   _____

   _____

6. From which selection did you learn the most about *Benjamin Franklin*? Why?

   _____

   _____

   _____

   _____

Making Text-to-World Connections
Lesson 10 and Lesson 11

You read a book review on pages 61–63 and an interview on pages 66–68. What things in the selections remind you of things or people in the real world? For example, is there a famous person that you admire? Do you know someone who has worked hard to reach a difficult goal? Write an idea from each selection. Then tell how it reminds you of something or someone in the world.

	Selection	World
"Good Work, Ben"		
"How Shocking, Ben Franklin"		

Answer these questions to tell more about the two selections and the world.

1. Ben Franklin invented the lightning rod. This helped many people. What is an invention today that helps many people? How does it help?

   _____

   _____

   _____

   _____

2. Ben Franklin traveled to Europe to get help for his own country. Do countries today turn to one another for assistance? Give an example.

   _____

   _____

   _____

   _____

Extend the Selections
Lesson 10 and Lesson 11

Now use your ideas to take the selections beyond the page!

1. Would you like to be a time-traveling reporter like Inez Sandoval? Where would you go? Whom would you interview? Why?

_____

_____

_____

_____

2. Imagine that Ben Franklin is applying for a job. What would he list on his resume? Write some things describing Ben's experience.

_____

_____

_____

_____

3. Ben Franklin had many inventions. Choose one of the following inventions or one of your own. Research the invention. Prepare an ad presenting the invention to the public for the first time.

   Inventions: blue jeans, bubble gum, cotton candy, escalator, ferris wheel, parachute, safety pin, yo-yo, zipper, refrigerator.

_____

_____

_____

_____

4. On another sheet of paper, draw and label one of Franklin's inventions. Or draw a sketch of the kite experiment. You might have to do some additional research.

UNIT 5 FICTION ⟷ NONFICTION

Preview

The first selection in Unit 5 is fiction, and the second selection is nonfiction.

In Lesson 13, you will read a FABLE, "The Crow and the Pitcher."

In Lesson 14, you will read a MAGAZINE ARTICLE, "Amazing Crows."

The two selections in Unit 5 share the topic of <u>crows</u>.

In Lesson 15, you will explore connections:

text to self

text to text

text to world

Fiction stories and nonfiction selections have different forms and purposes. They sometimes have similar elements or features, though. You will see this in the two selections in Unit 5.

Fiction stories come from a writer's imagination. They are made up. Most fiction stories have the following elements and form:

- **Setting:** when and where a story happens
- **Characters:** the people or animals in the story
- **Problem:** something that the characters must face and solve
- **Plot Events:** the things that happen in the story; the action
- **Resolution:** how the story ends

- When you read the fable "The Crow and the Pitcher" in Lesson 13, notice whom the story is about. These are the **characters**.

- Think about what **problem** the animal tries to solve in the fable. Then think about the steps the animal takes to solve the problem.

- Also watch for words that the writer uses in the fable to create **images** in your mind. Notice what senses these words relate to.

Nonfiction selections are about things that are real. Most nonfiction selections have the following elements and form:
  - **Introduction**: tells the topic
  - **Body**: gives main ideas and supporting details
  - **Conclusion**: sums up the main ideas and brings the selection to a close

- As you read Lesson 14, pay attention to whom the magazine article is about. A magazine article does not have characters, but it does have a **subject**.

- Pay attention to the **problems** that are solved in the magazine article.

- Notice the words that the writer uses in the article to create **images** in your mind. What senses do these words make you think of?

LESSON 13: Fable
"The Crow and the Pitcher"

Get Ready to Read

Learn About Fables

"The Crow and the Pitcher" is a fable.

> Fables are stories with a moral, or lesson. The characters are often animals that talk and act like people. In a fable, one animal often tricks another animal. Or the animal figures something out. This leads to the moral. The moral can guide readers to the best way to live.

Think About Vocabulary

When you read this fable, you may come across some new words. You may also find words used in unusual ways. Here are three words for you to know before you read.

drought: a long period without rain
pitcher: a container for liquids, usually with a handle and spout for pouring
peered: looked intently at; gazed

As you read the fable, circle at least three more words. Write the words and what they mean in the fable. Use a dictionary to check each meaning.

Show What You Know

This fable is about a crow who solves a difficult problem. Write the solution you found to a problem of your own.

Problem: _____

Solution: _____

_____

After you read the fable, you may want to add another solution.

Read "The Crow and the Pitcher"

The **fable** "The Crow and the Pitcher" is about a crow who faces a problem. As you read the fable, notice what the problem is and how the crow solves it. Be sure to watch for images. Think about what the moral teaches you about problem solving.

The Crow and the Pitcher

A bedraggled crow circled overhead. She was very thirsty. She was willing to drink even warm, muddy water, for she had not had a taste of water in days. The crow looked and looked and looked for just one little drop of water. But the rivers had all dried up. The lakes smelled of mud and rot. All the plants were brown and shriveled. It was the worst **drought** in years. There seemed to be no water anywhere. The crow was half dead. She needed water—and fast.

At last the thirsty crow spotted a **pitcher** resting on a picnic table. She tried to caw with delight, but only a dry croak came out of her mouth. It seemed that the pitcher had been left behind. Maybe some picnickers had forgotten it.

"Perhaps there is water in that pitcher," the crow croaked. She flew down and landed on the edge of the picnic table. Her toenails went *scritch, scritch, scritch* as she walked across the table to the pitcher. She **peered** inside. She could  see that the pitcher had water inside. But the neck of the pitcher was narrow. The crow could not stick her beak far enough into the pitcher to reach the water.

She tried and tried and tried again. But her beak just would not reach far enough to drink the water. No matter how she tried to squeeze her head into the pitcher, she could not reach the water.

"Oh, what am I to do?" moaned the crow. "I must have this water. But I can't reach it."

Then the crow noticed that the ground was covered with pebbles. She got an idea. Off the picnic table she hopped. She picked up a pebble in her beak. Then she flew with the pebble back to the pitcher. She dropped the pebble into the pitcher. She heard a pleasant *plink* as the pebble landed in the water.

The crow tried to reach the water, but still she could not reach it. So she hopped off the table again and picked up another pebble. She dropped this pebble into the water, *plink*, and again she tried to drink the water. Still the crow could not reach the water.

So the crow picked up another pebble and dropped it into the pitcher, *plink*. Then she took another pebble and dropped it into the pitcher. Then she took another pebble and dropped it into the pitcher. Then she took another pebble and dropped it into the pitcher. Then she took another pebble and dropped it into the pitcher. Then she took another pebble and dropped it into the pitcher. Then she took another pebble and dropped it into the pitcher. At last, at last, the crow saw that the water level had come up.

The water now reached the top of the pitcher. The crow was finally able to drink the water. She drank and drank and drank. When the water got too low for her beak to reach, she put more pebbles into the pitcher, *plink, plink, plink.* In this way, the crow was able to make the water rise a second time and a third time and a fourth time.

Although it took many hours, the crow was able to drink and drink and drink. She drank so much that she was no longer thirsty. "I'll have to remember this trick," thought the crow. "For tomorrow is another day, and I may be thirsty again."

Moral: Little by little does the trick.

Tell It in Your Words

Briefly retell the fable "The Crow and the Pitcher" in your own words. Tell who the characters are. Tell what happens in the story. Tell how the story ends.

_____

_____

_____

_____

_____

_____

_____

Check Your Understanding

Answer these questions to see how well you understood the fable "The Crow and the Pitcher." Circle the answers.

1. What is this fable mostly about?
   A a thirsty crow
   B a picnic table
   C a drought
   D a pile of pebbles

2. What happens when the crow tries to caw with delight?
   A The crow alerts the other animals about the pitcher of water.
   B The crow goes *plink, plink, plink*.
   C Only a dry croak comes out of her mouth.
   D The crow makes a *scritch, scritch, scritch* noise.

3. What does the crow do before she drops pebbles into the pitcher?
   A She drinks all the water out of the pitcher.
   B She tries to squeeze her head into the pitcher to drink.
   C She tips the pitcher over to spill out the water.
   D She is no longer thirsty.

4. Why does the crow drop pebbles into the pitcher?
   A to hear the pebbles go *plink, plink, plink*
   B to keep other animals from drinking the water
   C to splash water out of the pitcher for drinking
   D to make the water rise so that she can drink it

5. What might have happened to the crow if she had not found the pitcher of water?
   A She would have found water in a nearby lake.
   B She would have died.
   C She would have been fine until the end of the drought.
   D She would have collected rainwater to drink.

6. What is the purpose of this fable?
   A to show people how to survive in a drought
   B to show how big crows are
   C to show how pebbles can be used to raise water levels
   D to teach a way to solve problems

7. What is the main sense that *scritch, scritch, scritch* makes you think of?
   A taste
   B smell
   C hearing
   D sight

8. In the first paragraph, what does the word *shriveled* mean?
   A dried up
   B healthy
   C growing
   D fresh

LESSON 14: Magazine Article "Amazing Crows"

Get Ready to Read

Learn About Magazine Articles

"Amazing Crows" is a magazine article.

> Magazine articles tell about something in real life. The opening grabs your attention. Most of the article is made up of facts, examples, and reasons. Subheads in dark print tell about what is coming in each section. There are usually photos with captions. The ending sums up the article or gives a final detail.

Think About Vocabulary

When you read this article, you may come across some new words. You may also find words used in unusual ways. Here are three words for you to know before you read.

suburban: an area near a city where people live
June bug: a beetle that destroys farmers' crops
weevil: a beetle that destroys nuts, fruits, stems, and roots of plants

As you read the article, circle at least three more words. Write the words and what they mean in the article. Use a dictionary to check each meaning.

Show What You Know

This article is about crows. What do you already know about crows? What do they look like? What do they sound like? What have you seen them do? Write your own ideas in the web.

You can add to the web after you read the article.

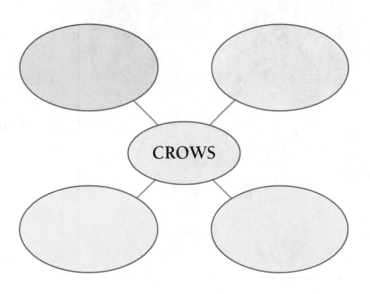

CROWS

Read "Amazing Crows"

"Amazing Crows" is a **magazine article**. As you read the article, pay attention to the things that make it a magazine article. Also notice the images that the writer uses to bring the article to life. Be aware of the many different kinds of problems that the crows solve.

Amazing Crows

If men had wings and black feathers, few of them would be clever enough to be crows.
—Henry Ward Beecher

Mr. Beecher was right. Crows are smart. In fact, they may be one of the smartest birds of all. Like people and some other mammals, crows use tools. Some crows make tools out of twigs. They tear off the leaves with their beaks. Then they break and twist the twig until it has a small hook at the end. They use this tool to remove tasty insects from holes in trees or from under leaves.

How Smart Are Crows?

Scientists gave one remarkable crow named Betty a straight piece of wire. Betty had never seen or used wire before. But she bent the wire into a hook. Then she used the hooked wire to reach down a pipe and remove a bucket of meat. Up until then, it was thought that only people could make tools out of objects they had never seen before.

After what Betty did, a Seattle scientist said of crows, "These guys are right up there with your dog."

But crows have even been known to outsmart dogs. Crows often eat in large groups on the ground. A few crows sit in the treetops watching. These are the lookouts. They will sound an alarm, *caw, caw, caw,* if danger approaches.

And if a dog tries to chase the feeding crows, one crow may fly just above the dog's nose. The crow almost seems to tease the dog. This crow may lead the dog away from the other crows who are eating on the ground. After a few minutes, a second crow will take a turn leading the excited dog in great circles. Then a third crow will replace the second. In this way, all of the crows get a chance to eat. And the pesky dog does not disturb their meal.

What Do Crows Eat?

What crows eat depends on where they live. Crows can live almost anywhere except dry deserts, cold mountaintops, and thick forests. They especially like farmland, orchards, city parks, rivers, streams, seashores, and towns.

Crows eat their weight in food every day. Can you imagine how much food you would eat if you ate your weight each day? Because crows need so much food, they are not picky eaters. They eat whatever they can find. They will eat corn and wheat and apples and nuts. They will eat fat grubs from your lawn or stinky garbage from landfills. If they live near the ocean, crows will eat raw clams. A crow will carry a clam high into the air and drop it on the hard rocks below. The shell will crack open, and the crow will swoop down to eat the meat inside.

Suburban crows have been known to watch a squirrel bury a peanut. As soon as the squirrel leaves, the crow digs up the peanut and eats it. Yes, crows are very clever animals.

Crows on the Farm

Many farmers do not like crows because crows eat their crops. Sometimes farmers put up scarecrows to keep crows away. But scarecrows do not work. Crows learn quickly that they have nothing to fear from scarecrows. While it is true that crows eat corn, they also help farmers. Crows eat insect pests such as **June bugs**, grasshoppers, grubs, and **weevils**. They also eat rodents such as mice and rats, which damage crops.

Crows in Your Neighborhood

Because crows are so common, chances are good that you will see one someday. When you do, pay special attention. The crow may amaze you with its clever actions.

Tell It in Your Words

Briefly summarize the magazine article "Amazing Crows" in your own words. Tell the most important ideas and any important details.

_____

_____

_____

_____

_____

_____

_____

Check Your Understanding

Answer these questions to see how well you understood the magazine article "Amazing Crows." Circle the answers.

1. What is the magazine article mostly about?
   A Crows can live almost anywhere.
   B Crows eat farmers' crops.
   C Crows can make tools.
   D Crows are very smart.

2. The story about crows leading a dog in circles shows that
   A crows do not like dogs.
   B dogs are smarter than crows.
   C crows can work together.
   D all dogs like to run.

3. What might a crow do right after a squirrel buries a peanut?
   A follow the squirrel home
   B tell other crows about the buried peanut
   C dig up the peanut and eat it
   D bury the peanut for later

4. Why do some crows drop clams from high distances?
   A to crack the shells open
   B to hit seagulls on the head
   C to play a game
   D to get exercise

5. How are crows in cities and crows on farms alike?
   A They both eat clams.
   B They both fear scarecrows.
   C They both eat their weight in food each day.
   D They both use tools to get buckets of meat.

6. In the next-to-the-last paragraph, you can tell that the word *grubs* means
   A muddy corn kernels.
   B insect pests.
   C rodents like rats and mice.
   D buried peanuts.

7. If you had a pet crow, you would probably be able to
   A teach it to say your name.
   B get it to chase dogs.
   C get it to build a scarecrow.
   D teach it tricks.

8. The writer of the magazine article probably
   A does not like crows.
   B has seen crows.
   C has never seen crows.
   D has taught crows to use tools.

FICTION & NONFICTION

LESSON 15: Connections

Making Text-to-Self Connections
Lesson 13

Reread the fable "The Crow and the Pitcher" on pages 79–81. What things in the fable remind you of things in your own life? Write one or two ideas from the fable. Tell how each reminds you of something in your own life. For example, have you ever been very thirsty? Have you ever solved a difficult problem? Have you worked at something little by little until you reached your goal?

Fable	Self

Answer the following questions to tell more about the fable.

1. Can you think of any other ways that the crow could have gotten to the water? Be clever. Write your ideas.

   _____

   _____

   _____

   _____

2. The crow thinks a lot like a human would think. How do you feel after you have solved a difficult problem? How did the crow probably feel?

   _____

   _____

   _____

   _____

FICTION & NONFICTION

Making Text-to-Self Connections
Lesson 14

Reread the magazine article "Amazing Crows" on pages 84–86. What things in the article remind you of things in your own life? Write one or two ideas from the article. Tell how each reminds you of something in your own life. For example, do you live in the city? Do you live in the country? Have you ever seen crows? Have you ever worked with others to reach a goal that would be hard to reach by yourself?

Magazine Article	Self

Answer the following questions to tell more about the magazine article.

1. A magazine article gives information. What facts or details did you learn that you did not know before? What did you find most amazing?

_____

_____

_____

_____

2. Crows are smart. What other smart animals do you know about? Name one other smart animal. Which of the two do you think is smarter? Why?

_____

_____

_____

_____

Making Text-to-Text Connections
Lesson 13 and Lesson 14

You read the fable "The Crow and the Pitcher" on pages 79–81. You read the magazine article "Amazing Crows" on pages 84–86. Answer these questions to tell about the two selections.

1. The crow is a **character** in the fable. Crows are the **subject** of the magazine article. Tell one way that the crows in the article are different from the crow in the fable. Write on the line in the diagram.

Crow in Fable
- *half dead*
- *alone*

Similar
- *good problem solvers*
- *clever*

Crows in Article
- *well-fed*
- _____

2. List a **problem** solved by a crow in each selection.

"The Crow and the Pitcher"	"Amazing Crows"

3. Some **images** can appeal to more than one of your senses. What senses can the images below make you think of?

   a. **Image:** Tear off the leaves with their beaks

   Senses: _____

   b. **Image:** She dropped this pebble into the water, *plink*.

   Senses: _____

FICTION & NONFICTION

4. Reread each selection. Look for imagery that appeals to the five senses. List one image for each sense in the chart below. Do not use the **images** listed in number 3 on page 90.

Sense	"The Crow and the Pitcher"	"Amazing Crows"
sight		
smell		
hearing		
touch		
taste		

5. What about "The Crow and the Pitcher" makes it a **fable**? What about "Amazing Crows" makes it a **magazine article**?

_____

_____

_____

_____

_____

6. How does each selection connect to the topic of *crows*?

_____

_____

_____

_____

_____

Making Text-to-World Connections
Lesson 13 and Lesson 14

You read a fable on pages 79–81 and a magazine article on pages 84–86. What things in the two selections remind you of things in the real world? For instance, how do people in your community feel about crows? Write an idea from each selection and tell how it reminds you of something in the world.

	Selection	World
"The Crow and the Pitcher"		
"Amazing Crows"		

Answer these questions to tell more about the two selections and the world.

1. People have often created big changes by working on one small change after another. Think about a big problem in the world today. What small things can be done to change the problem little by little?

   _____

   _____

   _____

2. Do you think animals can solve problems, have a sense of humor, or be like humans in other ways? Why or why not?

   _____

   _____

   _____

FICTION & NONFICTION

Extend the Selections
Lesson 13 and Lesson 14

Allow your creativity to take the selections beyond the page!

1. You are a writer. You want to write a fable that teaches others about a good way to live. What will your fable be about? What animal will you use to show the human problem? Fill in the chart below to tell about your fable.

What the Fable Is About	
An Animal with Human Traits	
A Problem the Animal Solves	
A Moral or Lesson	

2. Crows can live in many places. If you were a crow, where would you most like to live? Why? Write your ideas below.

_____

_____

_____

_____

3. If crows could talk to people, what would they tell them? What do crows admire about people? What do crows dislike about people?

_____

_____

_____

_____

4. On a separate sheet of paper, create an illustration for the magazine article about crows. In your illustration, show something amazing that a crow can do.

UNIT **6** FICTION ⟷ NONFICTION

Preview

The first selection in Unit 6 is fiction, and the second selection is nonfiction.

In Lesson 16, you will read a HISTORICAL FICTION story, "Antonia and the Great Molasses Flood."

In Lesson 17, you will read a BIOGRAPHY, "Henry Ford and the Model T."

The two selections in Unit 6 share the topic of <u>events that happened in the early 1900s.</u>

In Lesson 18, you will explore connections:

text to self

text to text

text to world

Fiction stories and **nonfiction** selections have different forms and purposes. They sometimes have similar elements or features, though. You will see this in the two selections in Unit 6.

Fiction stories come from a writer's imagination. They are made up. Most fiction stories have the following elements and form:

- **Setting:** when and where a story happens
- **Characters:** the people or animals in the story
- **Problem:** something that the characters must face and solve
- **Plot Events:** the things that happen in the story; the action
- **Resolution:** how the story ends

- When you read the historical fiction story "Antonia and the Great Molasses Flood" in Lesson 16, notice when and where the story takes place. This is the **setting**.

- Also think about the **order** in which the events happen in the story. What happens first, second, last, and so on?

- Finally, think about the **problems** the children in the story are faced with. How are they resolved?

Nonfiction selections are about things that are real. Most nonfiction selections have the following elements and form:
  - **Introduction**: tells the topic
  - **Body**: gives main ideas and supporting details
  - **Conclusion**: sums up the main ideas

- As you read the biography "Henry Ford and the Model T" in Lesson 17, pay attention to when and where the events happen. This is the **setting** of the biography.

- Also notice the **order** in which the events happen in the biography.

- Finally, pay attention to what this biography tells about **problems** that Henry Ford solves.

FICTION & NONFICTION

Get Ready to Read

Learn About Historical Fiction

"Antonia and the Great Molasses Flood" is a historical fiction story.

> Historical fiction stories tell about a real time in history. These stories blend facts with fiction. The people in a historical fiction story are often made up, but the events really happened. The setting is always a real time and place. The people behave like people from that time.

Think About Vocabulary

When you read this story, you may come across some new words. You may also find words used in unusual ways. Here are four words for you to know before you read.

elevated: raised
concrete: a hard material made of sand and crushed stone that are bonded together by cement
rivets: metal bolts that hold metal sheets together
seams: lines formed where two pieces of steel are bolted together

As you read the story, circle at least three more words. Write the words and what they mean in the story. Use a dictionary to check each meaning.

Show What You Know

This story is about an unusual event that really happened. The story involves molasses. Molasses is sweet and sticky and thick like syrup. In the box, write your ideas about what a molasses flood is.

After you read the story, you can add ideas to the box.

Molasses Flood

READ "Antonia and the Great Molasses Flood"

"Antonia and the Great Molasses Flood" is a **historical fiction** story about an event that really happened. As you read, notice when and where the story takes place. Also pay attention to the order in which the events happen. Notice what the problem is.

Antonia and the Great Molasses Flood

January 15, 1919, started out like any other day. Little did I know that it would become the most frightening day of my life. My name is Antonia, and I live in Boston. On that warm day, I was happy. My four brothers and I laughed and joked as we walked to school.

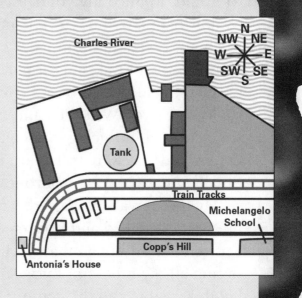

We went to the Michelangelo School. To get there, we walked in the shadow of the **elevated** train tracks. Every few minutes a train rumbled by above us. Where the tracks curved, we could see the Charles River ahead of us.

Soon we passed a giant storage tank. Its shiny steel sat in a **concrete** base. **Rivets**—it seemed like millions of them—held the tank together. Our teacher said the tank held 2.3 million gallons of molasses. Molasses is one of my favorite foods. It is sticky and sweet and improves the taste of almost everything.

We crossed Copp's Hill, and then we were at school. At 12:30 my brothers and I walked home for lunch. Suddenly we heard a rumbling sound. The ground shook beneath our feet. We turned and looked toward the sound. The huge tank of molasses was splitting at the **seams**. The rivets popped off, *POP! POP! POP!*  *POP!* Molasses spilled out of the tank and rolled toward us in a giant wave.

"Run!" I shouted to my brothers. We turned and ran as fast as we could. I pulled my youngest brother along with me. But we couldn't run fast enough. The molasses was moving at 35 miles per hour. It caught up to us. We were tossed up and tumbled along on top of the giant brown wave. I grasped my little brother's hand as tightly as I could. We were carried along like sticks in a river. We rolled and tumbled. Our mouths and faces were covered in thick goo. I could hardly breathe. We landed on the ground and were rolled around like pebbles on the beach. Finally the wave passed beyond us.

My throat was so clogged, I could not speak. I could barely breathe. I coughed and sputtered. I tried to wipe my eyes, but I was so covered in goo that wiping did no good. I stood up. I had to find all my brothers! I was still holding my little brother's hand. I tried to rub the goo out of his face. He started to cry.

I turned around. I saw my other brothers. One was already on his feet. One got to his knees and then wobbled to his feet. The third lay on the ground. I tried to run over to him, but my feet stuck in the goo. The goo sucked at my shoes. It took an enormous effort to pull just one foot out of the muck. But I was determined. I reached my brother and pulled him to his feet. He was crying, but he seemed OK.

The five of us held hands and slowly slogged home. My little brother's shoes were sucked into the muck, but we all made it home, where we washed and washed and washed.

Later I found out that the molasses covered several blocks of downtown Boston to a depth of two feet. It knocked down the elevated train tracks and smashed buildings. Firefighters managed to wash most of the molasses into the harbor, which turned brown. For weeks, however, everything in Boston was sticky—doorknobs, shop floors, train seats. And now, whenever I eat molasses, I am reminded of the most frightening day of my life.

Tell It in Your Words

Briefly retell the historical fiction story "Antonia and the Great Molasses Flood" in your own words. Tell who the most important characters are. Tell what happens in the story. Tell how the story ends.

_____

_____

_____

_____

_____

_____

_____

_____

Check Your Understanding

Answer these questions to see how well you understood the historical fiction story "Antonia and the Great Molasses Flood." Circle the answers.

1. What is this story mostly about?
   A a day at school
   B a walk to school
   C a frightening event
   D a girl and her brother

2. Why couldn't Antonia talk at first after the wave had passed?
   A Her face was in the dirt.
   B She was too scared.
   C She had molasses in her throat.
   D She didn't know what to say.

3. Which of these is true?
   A The tank held 3.5 million gallons.
   B The molasses traveled at 35 miles per hour.
   C The year was 1929.
   D The flood happened early in the morning.

4. Which event happened first?
   A The children held hands and slogged home.
   B The molasses tank split open.
   C Antonia was covered by molasses.
   D Antonia's brother started to cry.

5. What probably happened the day after the flood?
   A It snowed and the snow froze the molasses.
   B The children were afraid to look outside.
   C Rain washed the molasses away.
   D The cleanup continued.

6. What is the purpose of this story?
   A to tell about a real event in an exciting way
   B to warn people about the dangers of molasses
   C to show the proper way to live
   D to teach about a good way to store molasses

7. Look at the map on page 97. Antonia's house is
   A north of the tank.
   B east of the tank.
   C southwest of the tank.
   D right next to the Michelangelo School.

8. In the next-to-last paragraph, what does the word *slogged* mean?
   A ran quickly
   B crawled
   C jumped
   D walked slowly

LESSON 17: Biography
"Henry Ford and the Model T"

Get Ready to Read

Learn About Biographies

"Henry Ford and the Model T" is a biography.

A biography tells about the life of a real person. The person is named in the introduction. The body gives details about the person's life. The conclusion may give an interesting fact or tell about what the person accomplished.

Think About Vocabulary

When you read this biography, you may come across some new words. You may also find words used in unusual ways. Here are three words for you to know before you read.

repaired: fixed
plant: a factory where something is made
wages: money that workers earn for doing a job

As you read the biography, circle at least three more words. Write the words and what they mean in the biography. Use a dictionary to check each meaning.

Show What You Know

This biography is about Henry Ford, who made automobiles, or cars. How are cars today different from cars long ago?

In the top box, sketch the outline of an automobile today. In the bottom box, sketch the outline of a car from long ago.

You can add to your drawings after you read the biography.

Read "Henry Ford and the Model T"

"Henry Ford and the Model T" is a **biography**. As you read the biography, pay attention to when and where the events happen. Notice the order in which the events occur. Also, pay attention to the problems that Henry Ford solves.

Henry Ford and the Model T

Henry Ford was born in 1863. He lived on a farm near Detroit, Michigan. Henry helped his father on the farm. When he wasn't helping on the farm, he went to a one-room schoolhouse. In those days, most people did not go to high school. When Ford was 16, he walked eight miles to Detroit to get a job. He worked in a machine shop. He did not get paid much money. So he **repaired** clocks and watches at night. Henry was very good at putting things together.

Ford decided he wanted to make an automobile. At nights and on weekends, he worked in a shed behind his house. He was trying to build a car. His neighbors called him Crazy Henry. On June 4, 1896, at 2 A.M., Ford finished his first car. It had four bicycle wheels for tires. It didn't have brakes, and it couldn't go backwards. But it ran. For weeks, Ford drove his car around Detroit.

In 1903, Ford started the Ford Motor Company. He had 125 workers. That year the workers made 1,700 cars. But the cars were very expensive. Few people could afford to buy them. Ford wasn't happy. He wanted to build a car that almost anyone could buy.

Ford worked on a secret new car. He called it the Model T. This car was light in weight, powerful, and easy to drive. It cost $825. In 1909, eleven thousand Model Ts were sold. Unlike today's cars, the Model T had no heater, no air conditioner, no radio, and no turn signals. Some Model Ts had side curtains instead of windows. People had to work the windshield wipers by hand.

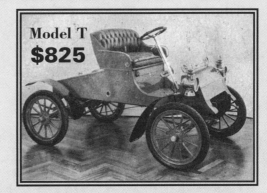

Model T $825

But soon, demand for these cars was so great that Ford's company could not keep up. Ford built a new **plant**. He wanted to make the cars even cheaper. In 1909, Ford said, "Everybody will be able to afford one, and about everybody will have one."

Ford decided that the fastest way to make a car was to have each worker do only one job. The workers stood still while the car parts moved along in front of them on a long belt. Some workers put on tires all day. Others painted. At first it took workers 12 hours to make a car. Later, it took only 5 hours. Eventually workers could make one car in $1\frac{1}{2}$ hours.

Many workers got bored. It was not fun putting tires on cars all day. So Ford paid his workers twice as much as before. He reduced the work day from 9 hours to 8 hours. Many people thought Ford was crazy. But Ford's plan worked. Workers were happier. And now, for the first time, Ford's workers could afford to buy Model Ts.

In 1912, the Model T cost $590. For the first time, a car cost less than one year's **wages**. By 1921, more than half of all cars sold were Model Ts. By 1925, a Model T cost only $260.

In 1927, the last Model T was made. But it had changed America. Cars were everywhere. City streets were jammed with cars. New roads were built just for cars. The auto age had begun.

Year	Cost of a Model T	Number of Cars Made
1909	$825	11,000
1911	$680	35,000
1913	$525	170,000
1915	$390	308,000
1917	$345	735,000
1921	$325	1,477,000
1925	$260	1,991,000

Tell It in Your Words

Briefly summarize the biography "Henry Ford and the Model T" in your own words. Tell the most important ideas and any important details in the biography.

_____

_____

_____

_____

_____

_____

_____

FICTION & NONFICTION

Check Your Understanding

Answer these questions to see how well you understood the biography "Henry Ford and the Model T." Circle the answers.

1. What is this biography mostly about?
   A Henry Ford's life in Detroit
   B Henry Ford's workers
   C the cost of Model Ts
   D how Henry Ford built a cheap, popular car

2. Ford's workers were bored doing one job all day. How did Ford solve this problem?
   A He had them do several jobs.
   B He let them work slower.
   C He doubled their wages.
   D He raised the price of Model Ts so that only the rich could afford them.

3. Where was Henry Ford born?
   A in 1863
   B on a farm near Detroit, Michigan
   C in the city of Detroit
   D on a farm near Chicago, Illinois

4. In the last paragraph on page 104, the word *jammed* means
   A filled.
   B sticky.
   C broken down.
   D noisy.

5. Which of these is an opinion?
   A In 1903, Ford started the Ford Motor Company.
   B A Model T cost $345 in 1917.
   C Model Ts did not have heaters.
   D Ford is the best American inventor.

6. From this biography, you can tell that Henry Ford
   A kept trying to lower prices.
   B did not like to work hard.
   C was not a good problem solver.
   D did not understand people.

7. Look at the chart on page 104. As prices of Model Ts went down, what happened to the number of cars made?
   A The number went up.
   B The number went down.
   C The number stayed the same.
   D You can't tell from the chart.

8. Look at the ad on page 103. Based on the price, around what year was the car in the ad built?
   A 1925
   B 1917
   C 1913
   D 1909

LESSON 18: Connections

Making Text-to-Self Connections
Lesson 16

Reread the historical fiction story "Antonia and the Great Molasses Flood" on pages 97–99. What things in the story remind you of things in your own life? Write one or two ideas from the story. Tell how each reminds you of something in your own life. For example, do you know what molasses tastes like?

Story	Self

Answer the following questions to tell more about the story.

1. How would you have felt if you had been caught by the molasses wave? Write your ideas.

   _____

   _____

   _____

   _____

2. If you were a rescue worker after this flood, what would you do? What would you see? How would you help?

   _____

   _____

   _____

   _____

FICTION & NONFICTION

Making Text-to-Self Connections
Lesson 17

Reread the biography "Henry Ford and the Model T" on pages 102–104. What things in the biography remind you of things in your own life? Write one or two ideas from the biography. Tell how each reminds you of something in your own life. For example, do you like to ride in cars? Have you ever made something you are proud of?

Biography	Self

Answer the following questions to tell more about the biography.

1. A biography tells about a famous person. What are some facts you learned about Henry Ford that you did not know before? Write them. Then put a check mark next to the fact that you found most interesting.

_____

_____

_____

_____

2. Do you think that modern cars or Model Ts are more amazing? Tell why you think so.

_____

_____

_____

_____

Making Text-to-Text Connections
Lesson 16 and Lesson 17

You read the historical fiction story "Antonia and the Great Molasses Flood" on pages 97–99. You read the biography "Henry Ford and the Model T" on pages 102–104. Answer these questions to tell about the two selections.

1. The **setting** is when and where a selection takes place. Write details about the settings in these two selections.

"Antonia and the Great Molasses Flood"	"Henry Ford and the Model T"
When:	When:
Where:	Where:

2. Henry Ford's first job did not pay him much money. How did he solve this **problem**?

_____

_____

_____

_____

3. List another **problem** and solution in each selection.

"Antonia and the Great Molasses Flood"	"Henry Ford and the Model T"

FICTION & NONFICTION

4. Below are some events that happened in the two selections.
   Tell what happened next in the **order** of events.

   a. **Event:** The molasses tank burst.
      What happened next: Antonia and her brothers were swept up by the molasses.

      What happened next: _____

      What happened next: _____

   b. **Event:** Henry Ford wants to make cars faster.
      What happened next: He had each worker do one job only.

      What happened next: _____

      What happened next: _____

      What happened next: _____

5. Both of these selections tell about real things that happened in history.
   The **historical fiction** story is a blend of fact and fiction. The **biography**
   gives mostly facts. Which method of telling about history do you like best?
   Why? Use examples to explain your ideas.

   _____

   _____

   _____

   _____

   _____

6. Both of these selections tell about *events that happened in the early 1900s.*
   What did you learn about life in America during this period?

   _____

   _____

   _____

   _____

   _____

Making Text-to-World Connections
Lesson 16 and Lesson 17

You read a historical fiction story on pages 97–99 and a biography on pages 102–104. What things in the two selections remind you of things in the real world? Think about what you've seen on television programs or read about in magazines. For instance, what inventions of today might change America like the automobile did? Have there been any disasters in your community? Write an idea from each selection and tell how it reminds you of something in the world.

	Selection	World
"Antonia and the Great Molasses Flood"		
"Henry Ford and the Model T"		

Answer these questions to tell more about the two selections and the world.

1. Tell what rescue workers did in a recent flood or other disaster that you've heard about.

_____

_____

_____

_____

2. Describe the good effects and the bad effects of automobiles today.

_____

_____

_____

_____

FICTION & NONFICTION

Extend the Selections
Lesson 16 and Lesson 17

Allow your creativity to take the selections beyond the page!

1. Pretend you are 90 years old. Someone has just written a biography about your life. What does the biography tell about?

_____

_____

_____

_____

_____

2. List several things that you think might have caused the molasses tank to burst. Use your imagination.

_____

_____

_____

_____

3. Pretend you are a worker making Model Ts. Do you like your job? Your wages? Write a diary entry describing a day in your life.

_____

_____

_____

_____

4. On a separate sheet of paper, draw a design for a new car of today. What amazing things can your car do? Include these amazing things in your drawing. Label your drawing.

FICTION & NONFICTION